PRENTICE HALL
EXPLORING
Physical Science

P9-DDJ-259

LABORATORY MANUAL

Prentice Hall
Englewood Cliffs, New Jersey
Needham, Massachusetts

Laboratory Manual
Annotated Teacher's Edition

PRENTICE HALL
Exploring Physical Science

© 1995 by Prentice-Hall, Inc., Englewood Cliffs, New Jersey 07632.
A Paramount Communications Company. All rights reserved. No part
of this book may be reproduced or transmitted in any form or by any
means, electronic or mechanical, including photocopying, recording,
or by any information storage and retrieval system, without
permission in writing from the publisher. Printed in the United States
of America.

ISBN 0-13-807141-1

3 4 5 6 7 8 9 10   98 97 96 95

Prentice Hall
A Paramount Communications Company
Englewood Cliffs, New Jersey 07632

Contents

© Prentice-Hall, Inc.

Overview of the Laboratory Manual

Science is an exciting area of study for the middle school and junior high-school student, and the *Prentice Hall Exploring Physical Science Laboratory Manual* helps bring forth this excitement through a variety of activities that are interesting and informative. The *Laboratory Manual* consists of Laboratory Investigations directly correlated to the information presented in each chapter of the *Prentice Hall Exploring Physical Science* textbook. The varied investigations and activities review information presented in each chapter and reinforce key concepts and scientific terms in an enjoyable and creative manner.

Thus, the *Laboratory Manual* is a companion text for your students, designed to help you in the teaching of the text material. This Annotated Teacher's Edition provides all the information needed to help you perform these investigations and activities with your students. It features answers to all Laboratory Investigations, annotations for general laboratory preparations, correlations to relevant pages in the student textbook, guidelines for laboratory safety, a comprehensive laboratory materials and equipment list, and addresses of suppliers of laboratory materials and equipment.

The *Laboratory Manual* contains only Laboratory Investigations that require a minimum of materials and equipment and that can be performed without an elaborate laboratory facility. Most equipment used in the investigations should be readily available at the school or can easily be obtained locally or through a supply house at minimal cost. In addition, the Laboratory Investigations require a minimum of preparation by the teacher, and most can be completed within a single class period.

It is strongly suggested that students be required to read the appropriate Laboratory Investigation one day prior to performing it in the laboratory. Furthermore, it is suggested that the students be asked to provide hypotheses to each problem presented in the Laboratory Investigation. You may want to write these hypotheses on the board before beginning the investigation. Then, after the students complete the investigation, go back and analyze each hypothesis. Make sure students realize that they are not being graded on their suggested hypotheses. Even scientists may discard a hypothesis after the data have been analyzed.

LABORATORY INVESTIGATION FORMAT

Each Laboratory Investigation is developed to strengthen the student's laboratory procedures, use of the scientific method, and problem-solving skills. The purpose of the Laboratory Investigations is also to provide a practical application of the material presented in the student textbook. The easy-to-follow format of each Laboratory Investigation allows the students to complete the investigations on their own, perhaps after an overview and brief explanation from you. This allows you to provide the necessary help to those individuals or groups of students who require teacher assistance. Each Laboratory Investigation is organized in the following manner.

Background Information

An overview is presented at the beginning of each Laboratory Investigation. This overview relates the Laboratory Investigation to a specific key concept presented in the student text or provides background information that the student will need in order to complete the lab.

Problem

Each Laboratory Investigation challenges the student by introducing a problem in the form of a question. Upon successful completion of the Laboratory Investigation, the student should be able to answer the initial question.

Materials

Each Laboratory Investigation contains a list of materials necessary to complete the lab. The quantity of materials necessary for each exercise has been designed for groups of students or an entire class. In general, groups of six students work best. A comprehensive alphabetical listing of necessary equipment and materials can be found on pages T10 through T14 of this Annotated Teacher's Edition.

Procedure

An easy-to-follow, step-by-step outline provides details necessary for the successful completion of the Laboratory Investigation by the students. In many of the Laboratory Investigations, drawings are included to help the students as they complete the lab.

Safety symbols are included next to those steps in the Procedure that require students to follow specific safety precautions. Students should be reminded that a safety symbol alerts them to follow appropriate safety precautions for that particular step in the procedure as well as in all following steps. For example, the first time an open flame is used, students will see the symbol of the open flame. Students should put on safety goggles for that particular step and continue to wear them throughout the investigation unless instructed to remove them.

Observations

In keeping with the traditional scientific method, Observations are asked for after the Procedure in each investigation. Observations often include filling in data tables and graphs, as well as answering general questions.

Analysis and Conclusions

Using observations and knowledge gained from reading the appropriate chapter in the textbook, students are asked to draw conclusions. Analysis and Conclusions allow students to tie together the Problem, Procedure, and Observations comprising the investigation they have performed.

Critical Thinking and Application

This section encourages students to use critical-thinking skills to answer a variety of questions based on the Laboratory Investigation and their textbook reading. Many questions emphasize possible applications of the experiment just performed and allow students to tie the investigation to real-life situations they may face or to situations a scientist might face.

© Prentice-Hall, Inc.

Going Further

Each Laboratory Investigation concludes with a section entitled Going Further. This section provides students with additional activities to investigate, which may be used as enrichment activities, supplementary activities, or alternative activities. Complete instructions for performing the additional activities are included so that individual students can perform the activities without additional teacher help.

Safety Symbols

On page 6 are several safety precaution symbols. A short paragraph describes what each symbol means and the safety precautions to take when the symbol appears in a Laboratory Investigation. These symbols immediately alert students to the need for special safety precautions. It is suggested that you make sure students are aware of the meaning of each symbol before starting any Laboratory Investigation.

Teacher Annotations

This Annotated Teacher's Edition allows the teacher the convenience of immediate reference to answers, suggestions, and additional instructions or precautions for the Laboratory Investigations provided in the *Laboratory Manual*. The annotations are printed in red on the pages corresponding to the student pages.

The Annotations provided for the Laboratory Investigation questions are

1. Specific objective answers, such as those provided in Observations, Analysis and Conclusions, and Critical Thinking and Application.
2. Anticipated student answers based on varied student data where there is an expected response.
3. Subjective answers to those questions that may provide a variety of responses. These will be marked by the statement "Answers will vary." The teacher should look for a logical response based on the observations and data collected by the students during the investigation.

Guidelines for Laboratory Safety

Safety should be an integral part of the planning, preparation, and implementation of a laboratory program. Both the teacher and the student are responsible for creating and maintaining an enjoyable, instructional, and safe environment in the laboratory.

GENERAL SAFETY CONSIDERATIONS

Emphasis on proper safety precautions for each Laboratory Investigation is an essential part of any pre-laboratory discussion. Prior to each investigation, demonstrate the proper use of the required equipment. Demonstrate any potentially hazardous procedure used in that investigation. Always wear the required safety protective devices during the demonstrations and the investigations. If students are required to wear safety goggles, you and any visitors to the class must also wear them.

During an investigation, move about the laboratory to keep a constant watch for potentially dangerous situations. Behavior that is inappropriate to a laboratory situation should be curtailed immediately. Wild play and practical jokes are forbidden in the laboratory. Once students realize that the practice of safety is a required part of the course, they will accept a serious approach to laboratory work.

Any Laboratory Investigation a student performs should have your prior approval. Students should never work in the laboratory without adult supervision. At the conclusion of the investigation, cleanup should follow authorized guidelines for waste disposal. The laboratory should be restored to a safe condition for the next class.

CLASSROOM ORGANIZATION

Furniture and equipment in the laboratory should be arranged to minimize accidents. Assign students to laboratory stations. Each station should be equipped with a flat-topped table and laboratory bench. Do not use desks with slanted tops. Provide several locations where students can obtain needed supplies. Control traffic flow in the room to prevent collisions between students who are carrying or handling equipment. Tell students to leave their personal property in a designated location, away from the laboratory stations. Do not use the floor and benches for storage areas. Stress that good housekeeping is important in maintaining safe laboratory conditions. Students should keep all laboratory work areas clean. Unnecessary papers, books, and equipment should be removed from working areas.

Be sure that water faucets, hot plates, gas outlets, and alcohol or Bunsen burners are turned off when not in use.

SAFETY EQUIPMENT

Any classroom where Laboratory Investigations are performed should contain at least one each of the following pieces of safety equipment: (1) fire extinguisher, (2) fire blanket, (3) fire alarm, (4) phone or intercom to the office, (5) eyewash station, (6) safety shower, (7) safety hood, and (8) first-aid kit. If any of these basic pieces of safety equipment are not available, you may need to modify your laboratory program until the situation is remedied.

Make sure students know the location and proper use of all safety equipment. Where appropriate and practical, have students handle or operate the equipment so that they become familiar with it. Make sure all safety equipment is in good working order. All malfunctions should be promptly reported in writing to the proper school or district administrator.

Fire equipment At the beginning of the school year, you may wish to give each student the opportunity to actually operate a fire extinguisher, as the sound and action of a CO_2 fire extinguisher can be quite alarming to those who have never used one. You may also want to have students practice smothering imaginary flames on one another with the fire blanket.

Eyewash station The eyewash station should be used if chemicals are splashed onto the face or eyes. The exposed area should be left in the running water for five to ten minutes.

Safety shower The shower is used when chemicals have been spilled on a student's body or clothing. The student should stand under the shower until the chemical is completely diluted. Have a bathrobe or some type of replacement clothing handy in case the student's clothing is so badly contaminated that it must be removed.

You may want to set up one or two spill kits in your laboratory. The contents of a spill kit are used to neutralize chemicals such as acids and bases so that they can be cleaned up more easily. Baking soda (sodium bicarbonate) can be used to neutralize acids. Vinegar (acetic acid) can be used

© Prentice-Hall, Inc.

to neutralize bases. Commercial spill kits for acids, bases, and a number of other chemicals are available from supply houses.

Safety hood Use a safety hood whenever students are working with volatile or noxious chemicals. Make sure that the room is well ventilated when students are using any kind of chemicals or are working with preserved specimens. Warn students of the flammability and toxicity of various chemicals.

First-aid kit A typical first-aid kit contains an assortment of antiseptics, bandages, gauze pads, and scissors. Most also contain simple instructions for use. Be sure to read the instructions if you are not familiar with basic first-aid procedures. A first-aid kit should be taken on all field trips. For field trips, you may wish to add such items as a bee-sting kit, meat tenderizer, tweezers, and calamine lotion. Do not dispense medication (including aspirin).

CLEANUP

Before beginning an investigation, instruct students in the proper cleanup procedures. Mark certain containers for the disposal of wastes and the collection of soiled glassware and equipment. Have students dispose of broken glassware in a separate trash container. Before the end of the laboratory period, have students unplug microscopes and other pieces of equipment and put them away in their proper location. Have students wash glassware, wipe up spills, and do whatever else is necessary to clean up their work area. At the conclusion of the Laboratory Investigation, the room should be restored to a clean and safe condition for the next class. You may wish to institute a policy of not dismissing the class until the laboratory area meets with your approval.

PREPARATIONS AND THE STORAGE ROOM

Reagents stored in the stockroom should be clearly labeled and stored safely. Take inventory of reagents frequently and keep up-to-date records of their use. Check local and state regulations for maximum permissible amounts of reagents allowed in school. In case of fire or vandalism, inform the authorities of possible hazards to the community. Keep all chemicals in a locked storage area that is accessible only to you or individuals under your direct supervision.

Some chemicals are incompatible and should be stored separately. For information on the safe storage of chemicals, refer to *Safety in Academic Chemistry Laboratories,* 5th edition (1990), pub-

lished by the American Chemical Society. This publication may be obtained from The American Chemical Society, 1155 16th Street, N.W., Washington, DC 20036. Check local and state laws for regulations on storage of flammable liquids. The National Fire Protection Association recommends that flammable liquids be stored in vented, flame-resistant cabinets. Store large containers near floor level. Make sure that storage shelves have a raised lip at the front to prevent containers from sliding forward.

HAZARDOUS MATERIALS

Some reagents can be explosive and should not be on the premises. If found, they should be removed by trained fire or police bomb squads or by other qualified officials.

Known carcinogens and probable carcinogens have frequently been found in stockrooms and should be removed by health authorities or a licensed commercial company. If you have doubts about the hazards of any reagent in the stockroom, contact an appropriate agency (NIOSH or a local health agency).

Known carcinogens commonly found in school science laboratories include the following:

arsenic powder	formaldehyde
arsenic trichloride	lead arsenate
arsenic pentoxide	benzene
arsenic trioxide	chromium powder
asbestos	sodium arsenate
benzidine	

Possible carcinogens include the following:

acrylonitrile	cadmium powder
cadmium chloride	cadmium sulfate
carbon tetrachloride	chloroform
ethylene oxide	nickel powder

Exercise great care in using refrigerators. Never store flammable liquids in a refrigerator unless it is explosion-proof. Do not store food where microbial cultures are stored. Clean refrigerators frequently and safely discard old material.

LABORATORY GLASSWARE

Probably the most common school laboratory accidents involve cuts from chipped or broken glassware and burns from hot glassware. Discard any glassware that has a crack or chip. Use only borosilicate glassware. Fire-polish the ends of glass tubing. Allow hot glassware to cool on a hot pad for several minutes before picking it up. If an accident should happen, first aid for minor cuts and burns is immersion in cool running water. For cuts that are bleeding heavily, apply pressure with folded toweling or gauze. Call a health professional immediately.

To insert glass tubing into a stopper, lubricate the stopper hole and the tubing. Wrap the tubing in several layers of toweling and gently work the tubing into the stopper, using a twisting motion and keeping the hands as close together as possible. Wear heavy gloves. Remove the tubing in the same manner as soon as possible. Tubing that is stuck is nearly impossible to remove without cutting the stopper.

To avoid unwanted cultures, clean glassware frequently by using laboratory detergent. Most deposits can be removed with dilute hydrochloric acid or sodium hydroxide solution. Do not permit students to eat or drink from laboratory glassware.

Measuring small amounts of liquids with pipettes is common in investigations. But never pipette by mouth. Use rubber suction bulbs designed for use with pipettes or pipette fillers.

SAFETY PROCEDURES WITH MICROBIAL CULTURES

Never culture pathogenic bacteria. However, treat all bacterial cultures as if they are pathogenic. Firmly seal with clear tape any bacterial plates that are used for student inspection. For sterilization, use a high-temperature gas flame rather than an alcohol burner or candle flame.

Cultures should be killed before disposal. Autoclave all cultures and contaminated glassware at 15 pounds pressure per square inch (103.4 Pa) for 20 minutes. Disposable plates should be incinerated.

SAFETY PROCEDURES WITH MICROSCOPES

Never use direct sunlight as a light source for the microscope. The lenses may concentrate the light and cause permanent retinal damage. With a soft cloth dipped in isopropyl alcohol, clean the eyepiece of each microscope between viewers. Make sure any electrical cords are out of the main traffic pattern of the classroom.

SAFETY PROCEDURES WITH DISSECTIONS

Handle sharp and pointed instruments with care. Make sure the specimen is firmly secured on a dissection tray or cutting board. Caution students never to dissect a hand-held specimen. Make sure that the scalpels and scissors are sharp and adequate for the job. If razor blades are used for cutting tissues for slide mounts, use only single-edge noninjectable blades. Dissecting instruments should not be removed from the laboratory and should be stored in a locked cabinet.

Formaldehyde has been identified as a carcinogen and mutagen. Any formaldehyde-preserved specimens in the stockroom or classroom should be removed from the school site by qualified health authorities or a licensed commercial company. Specimens are now sold in alternative preservatives. Follow the instructions on the package for preparing specimens for dissection. Most should be rinsed in running water before use. Some may need to be soaked in water overnight if the preservative is particularly strong smelling. Specimens that have not been preserved should be used sparingly and only for a short time. Use only healthy specimens. Instruct students to wear masks and gloves to guard against infection. After dissection, specimens should be discarded in separate containers that can be transported to an incineration site.

FIELD STUDIES

Before taking the students on a field study, examine the area for possible safety hazards. Look for terrain or water hazards and poisonous plants and animals. Obtain the necessary written permission from parents and school authorities. Instruct students on proper dress and behavior. Make sure that students are thoroughly familiar with the investigations they are to conduct. If students are to form small groups, decide in advance when and where they will reassemble. Do not allow any student to travel alone.

Identify any students who have special health problems, especially allergies. Alert these students to potential hazards. Be sure they are adequately prepared to deal with emergencies.

Laboratory Materials and Equipment

Note: Safety equipment has not been listed. It is recommended that a laboratory apron, safety goggles, and heat-resistant gloves be worn when required.

Item	Quantity per Group	Laboratory Investigation
Acid		
hydrochloric		
concentrated	8.3 mL	23
1 M	5 drops	7
	1 bottle	20, 24
sulfuric, 2 M	1 L	19
Alcohol		
ethyl	50 mL	4
isopropyl	25 mL	26
Aluminum		
disk with hole	1	45
foil	15 cm × 15 cm	7
	several sheets	57
shot	10 g	20
Ammeter, 0 to 1-A	1	49
Antacid		
several types (noneffervescent)	1 package of each	24
tablets	1 package	25
Ball		
Ping-Pong™	1	42
rubber, air-filled	1	42
sponge	1	42
tennis	1	42
Balance		
centigram	1	36
triple-beam	1	3, 4, 5, 8, 9, 10, 11, 18, 21, 44, 45
Battery		
1.5-V dry cell	1	48, 49, 52, 53
6-V dry cell	1	19
Beaker	1	33
	3	27
100-mL	1	24, 36
	2	1
	4	43
250-mL	1	5, 8, 10, 45
	2	2, 21
400-mL	1	9, 26
	2	6
	4	43
600-mL	1	19
Bicycle	1	30
Bleach, liquid	1 bottle	27
Boiling chips	several	26
Book	1	37, 38
Brass disk with hole	1	45
Bunsen burner	1	2, 7, 8, 9, 10, 17, 18, 23, 26, 43
Buret, 25 mL	1	33
Calorimeter	1	45
Can		
coffee with plastic lid	1	61
coffee	2	46
overflow	1	5
296-mL tin and lid	1	44
1.4-L tin	1	44
Can opener	1	44
Candle		
birthday	1	7
utility	1	31, 44, 61
Capacitor, 2000 to 6000 microfarads	1	28
Carbon grains	500 g	52
Cardboard	1	27
6 cm × 6 cm	1	61
corrugated		
12 cm × 12 cm	1	46
30 cm × 30 cm	1	35, 58, 59

Item	Quantity per Group	Laboratory Investigation
Celsius thermometer	1	6, 8, 9, 26, 43, 44,
	2	1, 45, 46
	3	57
Chemicals		
aluminum oxide	small quantity	22
barium nitrate, solution	dropper bottle	14
calcium nitrate, solution	dropper bottle	14
calcium oxide	small quantity	22
chromium oxide	small quantity	22
cobalt oxide	small quantity	22
copper sulfate, solution	solution bottle	15
lead acetate, solution	solution bottle	15
lead nitrate	100 g	21
magnesium nitrate, solution	dropper bottle	14
manganese dioxide	5 g	16, 22
potassium carbonate, solution	dropper bottle	14
potassium chromate, solution	dropper bottle	14
potassium iodide, solution	5 bottles	21
potassium nitrate	25 mL	8
	30 g	9
potassium sulfate, solution	dropper bottle	14
silicon dioxide	small quantity	22
silver nitrate, 0.1 M	dropper bottle	7
sodium chloride	small quantity	17
sodium hydroxide	4 g	23
strontium nitrate, solution	dropper bottle	14
zinc sulfate, solution	solution bottle	15
Clamp	1	34, 38
burette	1	33
test-tube	1	6, 7, 10, 26
	2	19
Clay, modeling	1 large piece	3, 7
Cleaning products, liquid, 4 types	1 bottle of each	25
Clips	12	53
alligator	2	52
paper		
large	2	34
Clock with second hand	1	28, 37, 46
Compass	1	51
Copper		
powder	small quantity	18
strip, 10-cm	1	15
30-cm	2	52
wire	1 cm	20
Cord	2 m	41
Cork	1	5, 47
Cup, plastic	1	52
Dropper, medicine	1	24, 25, 55
	2	23
Drum	1	56
Die	1	13
Ethylene glycol	25 mL	26
Evaporating dish	1	2, 17, 18
Flour	cup	12
Forceps	1	10
Fruit juice, three types	5 mL of each	25
Funnel	1	2
Glass, plate		
square, 1.2 cm thick	1	55
7 cm × 7 cm × 6 cm	1	59
Gloves, heat resistant	1 pair	6, 9, 23, 43
Graduated cylinder		
10-mL	1	16, 20, 23, 25
25-mL	1	36
100-mL	1	1, 2, 3, 8, 9, 19, 21, 43, 44
	4	4
Hall's carriage, skateboard or rollerskate	1	29
Hole puncher	1	35
Hook, pegboard	1	35

© Prentice-Hall, Inc.

Item	Quantity per Group	Laboratory Investigation
Hose, rubber	1	55
Hot plate	1	6, 45
Hydrogen peroxide, 3%	1 bottle	16, 22
Ice		
crushed	400 mL	26
cube	1	44
	several	1, 8
Index card	1	50
Insulating pad	1	7
Iron		
bar	1	3
cube	1	3
filings	1 bottle	50
nail	1	20
powder	5 g	10
Jar		
1-L with lid	1	31
small	3	57
Lamp, 1.5-V with sockets	1	48, 52
	3	49, 53
Lead strip, 10-cm	1	15
sinker	1	31, 36
disk with hole	1	45
Lens		
concave with holder	1	60
convex with focal point of 10 to 15 cm with holder	1	60
hand	1	10
Light source,	1	55
100-W	1	46
with holder	1	60
Line, nylon fishing	1 m	40
Litmus paper		
blue	1 package	23
red	1 package	23
Magnesium ribbon, 1-cm	1	7
	5	20
Magnet	1	10, 12
bar	1	51
	2	50
ceramic	2	12
Magnifying glass	1	23
Matches	1 box	7, 10, 16, 19, 31, 44, 61
Metal object	1	36
Methyl orange indicator solution	1 bottle	24
Meterstick clamp or holder	1	39, 60
Mineral	1	5
Mirror with support	1	58
pocket	2	61
Mortar and pestle	1	24
Oak tag, heavy grade	1	61
Oil, salad	1 bottle	4
Paper	1 sheet	7, 54
construction		
colored, 30 cm × 20 cm	1	12
heavy black	1 sheet	46
	several sheets	57
heavy white	1 sheet	46
filter	1 piece	2
graph	1 sheet	9, 13, 26
	several sheets	29
notebook	1 sheet	14
waxed	large piece	61
weighing	1 sheet	8, 21
white, unlined	several sheets	55, 58, 59
50 cm × 20 cm	1	12
Paradichlorobenzene crystals	4 g	6
	small quantity	17

Item	Quantity per Group	Laboratory Investigation
Pegboard	1	28, 35, 53
Pencil	1	12, 35, 54
colored	2	6, 46
glass-marking	1	1, 6, 27, 43
wax	1	4
Phenolphthalein, 1% solution	1 mL	23, 25
Pins, straight	several	47, 58, 59
Plate, pie	1	33
spot	1	14
Posterboard, strips		
20 cm × 2 cm	1	12
30 cm × 2 cm	2	12
Power supply, DC	1	28
Protractor	1	58, 59
Pulley		
double tandem	2	40
single	2	40
Reflector, automobile headlight with 2 holes punched in rim	1	47
Ring stand	1	26, 33, 38
	2	19
with ring	1	2, 9, 17, 18, 23, 27, 34, 36, 40, 44, 46
Ripple tank	1	55
Rock	1	5
Rope, measuring	1	56
Rubber band	1	61
Rubber cement	1	61
Ruler		
metric	1	3, 12, 29, 35, 44, 55, 58, 59
meterstick	1	29, 30, 33, 34, 38, 39, 42
with support stands		60
Salt, table	small scoopful	4, 7
Salt/sand mixture	10 g	2
Sand	several kg	57
Sandpaper	1 sheet	15, 32
Scale, spring, 20 N	1	27, 32, 38, 39, 40
Scissors	1	27, 35, 46, 61
Scoop	1	7, 10, 18
Screen, image with holder	1	60
Screw		
machine	several	53
wood	several	47
Shoe box with cover, filled with small objects	1	11
Spring	1	34
Stirring rod, glass	1	8, 9, 21, 23, 24, 25, 44
Stopper, rubber	1	5
2-hole	1	26
Stopwatch	2	30
capable of one-tenth second timing	1	56
String	(see Investigation)	31, 33, 35, 38, 39, 45
heavy	65 cm	37
Sulfur powder	3 g	10
Switch, knife	1	28, 49
double pole-double throw	1	53
single pole-single throw	3	53
Tables	2	37
Tape	roll	12, 57
masking	roll	13, 15, 29, 30
14-cm strips	2	46
Target platform with ramp	1	12
Test materials	(see Investigation)	48
Test tube	1	6, 10, 47
	2	7, 8, 16, 17
	4	23, 25
	5	20
	7	22
	9	15

© Prentice-Hall, Inc.

Item	Quantity per Group	Laboratory Investigation
medium-sized	4	9
large	3	26
Pyrex	1	47
Test-tube brush	1	25
Test-tube holder	1	8
Test-tube rack	1	6, 7, 9, 15, 16, 20, 25, 26
Thread	1 spool	36, 50
cotton	150 cm	27
cotton-covered polyester	150 cm	27
polyester	150 cm	27
Timer	1	33
recording with tape	1	29
Tongs	1	9, 18
beaker	1	2
Tripod	1	43
Tubing		
right-angle glass	1	26
rubber	40 cm	26
Vinegar, white, 5%	20 mL	25
Voltmeter, DC	1	28
0 to 3V	1	49
Washers	15	34
Watch glass	1	7
Water, distilled	1 L	24
Weight	1	35
100-g	1	34
500-g with hook	1	33
0.5-kg	1	39, 41
1-kg	1	39, 40, 41
Wire	1.5 m	33
bell	20 cm	19
connecting	21 pieces	28, 49
	4 m	51
30-cm long	3	52
Wire gauze	1	2, 9, 17, 18, 23,
with ceramic center	1	36, 43
Wire stripper	1	19
Wood		
block	several	55
block, 3-cm wide and 1 cm thick	2	47
30 cm × 15 cm	1	47
rectangle with metal eye	1	32
board, 1 m × 15 cm	1	38
cylinder, 10-cm long	1	4
piece, 10-cm long	2	50
rods	4	37
splints	2	16, 19
Zinc		
mossy	10 g	20
pieces	1 g	23
strip, 10-cm long	1	15

Suppliers of Laboratory Materials and Equipment

Analytical Scientific
11049 Bandera Road
San Antonio, TX 78250

Apple Computer, Inc.
20525 Mariani Avenue
Cupertino, CA 95014

Arbor Scientific
P.O. Box 2750
Ann Arbor, MI 48106-2750

Carolina Biological Supply Company
2700 York Road
Burlington, NC 27215

Central Scientific Company
  (CENCO)
3300 Cenco Parkway
Franklin Park, IL 60131

Chem Scientific, Inc.
67 Chapel Street
Newton, MA 02158

Connecticut Valley Biological
  Supply Company, Inc.
P.O. Box 326
82 Valley Road
Southampton, MA 01073

Delta Biologicals
P.O. Box 26666
Tucson, AZ 85726-6666

Edmund Scientific Company
101 East Gloucester Pike
Barrington, NJ 08007-1380

Fisher Scientific Company
Educational Materials Division
4901 West LeMoyne Street
Chicago, IL 60651

Flinn Scientific, Inc.
P.O. Box 219
131 Flinn Street
Batavia, IL 60510

Forestry Suppliers, Inc.
P.O. Box 8397
205 West Rankin Street
Jackson, MS 39284-8397

Frey Scientific Company
905 Hickory Lane
Mansfield, OH 44905

General Supply Corporation
P.O. Box 9347
Jackson, MS 39206

Grau-Hall Scientific Corporation
6501 Elvas Avenue
Sacramento, CA 95819

Hach Company
P.O. Box 389
Loveland, CO 80539

Harvard Apparatus Company
22 Pleasant Street
So. Natick, MA 01760

Hubbard Scientific Company
1120 Halbleib Road
Chippewa Falls, WI 54729

Ideal School Supply Company
11000 South Lavergne Avenue
Oak Lawn, IL 60453

Kons Scientific Company, Inc.
P.O. Box 3
Germantown, WI 53022-0003

La Pine Scientific Company
13636 Western Avenue
P.O. Box 780
Blue Island, IL 60406

Lab-Aids, Inc.
17 Colt Court
Ronkonkoma, NY 11779

Learning Spectrum
1390 Westridge Drive
Portola Valley, CA 94028

Learning Things, Inc.
P.O. Box 436
68A Broadway
Arlington, MA 02174

Leica, Inc.
111 Deer Lake Road
Deerfield, IL 60015

William A. Lemberger Company
2500 Waukau Avenue
Oshkosh, WI 54903

McKilligan Supply Corporation
435 Main Street
Johnson City, NY 13790

Ben Meadows Company
3589 Broad Street
Chamblee, GA 30341

Nasco
901 Janesville Avenue
Fort Atkinson, WI 53538

Nasco West, Inc.
P.O. Box 3837
Modesto, CA 95352

National Teaching Aids, Inc.
1845 Highland Avenue
New Hyde Park, NY 11040

Niles Biological
9298 Elder Creek Road
Sacramento, CA 95829

Nutritional Biochemicals
  Corporation
26201 Miles Road
Cleveland, OH 44128

Parco Scientific Company
P.O. Box 189
316 Youngstown-Kingsville Road
Vienna, OH 44473

Phipps and Bird, Inc.
8741 Landmark Road
Richmond, VA 23261

Sargent-Welch Scientific Company
911 Commerce Court
Buffalo Grove, IL 60089

Schoolmasters Science
P.O. Box 1941
745 State Circle
Ann Arbor, MI 48106

Science Kit and Boreal Labs
777 East Park Drive
Tonawanda, NY 14150

© Prentice-Hall, Inc.

Suppliers of Laboratory Materials and Equipment

Southern Precision Instrument
    Company
3419 East Commerce Street
San Antonio, TX 78220

Southwestern Biological Supply
    Company
P.O. Box 4084
Dallas, TX 75208

Spectrum Educational Supplies
    Limited
125 Mary Street
Aurora, Ontario, Canada L4G 1G3

Swift Instruments, Inc.
P.O. Box 562
San Jose, CA 95106

Triarch, Inc.
P.O. Box 98
Ripon, WI 54971

Ward's Natural Science
    Establishment Inc.
P.O. Box 92912
5100 West Henrietta Road
Rochester, NY 14692-9012

Wildlife Supply Company
301 Cass Street
Saginaw, MI 48602

Wilkens-Anderson Company
4525 West Division Street
Chicago, IL 60651

Exploring Physical Science

LABORATORY MANUAL

Prentice Hall
Englewood Cliffs, New Jersey
Needham, Massachusetts

Laboratory Manual

PRENTICE HALL
Exploring Physical Science

© 1995 by Prentice-Hall, Inc., Englewood Cliffs, New Jersey 07632.
A Paramount Communications Company. All rights reserved. No part of
this book may be reproduced or transmitted in any form or by any means,
electronic or mechanical, including photocopying, recording, or by any
information storage and retrieval system, without permission in writing
from the publisher. Printed in the United States of America.

ISBN 0-13-807133-0

2 3 4 5 6 7 8 9 10   98 97 96 95 94

Prentice Hall
A Paramount Communications Company
Englewood Cliffs, New Jersey 07632

Contents

© Prentice-Hall, Inc.

Safety Symbols

All the investigations in this *Laboratory Manual* have been designed with safety in mind. If you follow the instructions, you should have a safe and interesting year in the laboratory. Before beginning any investigation, make sure you read the safety rules that follow.

The eight safety symbols below appear next to certain steps in some of the investigations in this *Laboratory Manual*. The symbols alert you to the need for special safety precautions. The description of each symbol below tells you which precautions to take whenever you see the symbol in an investigation.

 ### Glassware Safety

1. Whenever you see this symbol, you will know that you are working with glassware that can easily be broken. Take particular care to handle such glassware safely. And never use broken or chipped glassware.
2. Never heat glassware that is not thoroughly dry. Never pick up any glassware unless you are sure it is not hot. If it is hot, use heat-resistant gloves.
3. Always clean glassware thoroughly before putting it away.

 ### Fire Safety

1. Whenever you see this symbol, you will know that you are working with fire. Never use any source of fire without wearing safety goggles.
2. Never heat anything—particularly chemicals—unless instructed to do so.
3. Never heat anything in a closed container.
4. Never reach across a flame.
5. Always use a clamp, tongs, or heat-resistant gloves to handle hot objects.
6. Always maintain a clean work area, particularly when using a flame.

 ### Heat Safety

Whenever you see this symbol, you will know that you should put on heat-resistant gloves to avoid burning your hands.

 ### Chemical Safety

1. Whenever you see this symbol, you will know that you are working with chemicals that could be hazardous.
2. Never smell any chemical directly from its container. Always use your hand to waft some of the odors from the top of the container toward your nose—and only when instructed to do so.
3. Never mix chemicals unless instructed to do so.
4. Never touch or taste any chemical unless instructed to do so.
5. Keep all lids closed when chemicals are not in use. Dispose of all chemicals as instructed by your teacher.
6. Immediately rinse with water any chemicals, particularly acids, that get on your skin and clothes. Then notify your teacher.

 ### Eye and Face Safety

1. Whenever you see this symbol, you will know that you are performing an experiment in which you must take precautions to protect your eyes and face by wearing safety goggles.
2. When you are heating a test tube or bottle, always point it away from you and others. Chemicals can splash or boil out of a heated test tube.

 ### Sharp Instrument Safety

1. Whenever you see this symbol, you will know that you are working with a sharp instrument.
2. Always use single-edged razors; double-edged razors are too dangerous.
3. Handle any sharp instrument with extreme care. Never cut any material toward you; always cut away from you.
4. Immediately notify your teacher if your skin is cut.

 ### Electrical Safety

1. Whenever you see this symbol, you will know that you are using electricity in the laboratory.
2. Never use long extension cords to plug in any electrical device. Do not plug too many appliances into one socket or you may overload the socket and cause a fire.
3. Never touch an electrical appliance or outlet with wet hands.

 ### Animal Safety

1. Whenever you see this symbol, you will know that you are working with live animals.
2. Do not cause pain, discomfort, or injury to an animal.
3. Follow your teacher's directions when handling animals. Wash your hands thoroughly after handling animals or their cages.

Science Safety Rules

One of the first things a scientist learns is that working in the laboratory can be an exciting experience. But the laboratory can also be quite dangerous if proper safety rules are not followed at all times. To prepare yourself for a safe year in the laboratory, read over the following safety rules. Then read them a second time. Make sure you understand each rule. If you do not, ask your teacher to explain any rules you are unsure of.

Dress Code

1. Many materials in the laboratory can cause eye injury. To protect yourself from possible injury, wear safety goggles whenever you are working with chemicals, burners, or any substance that might get into your eyes. Never wear contact lenses in the laboratory.
2. Wear a laboratory apron or coat whenever you are working with chemicals or heated substances.
3. Tie back long hair to keep it away from any chemicals, burners, and candles, or other laboratory equipment.
4. Remove or tie back any article of clothing or jewelry that can hang down and touch chemicals and flames.

General Safety Rules

5. Read all directions for an experiment several times. Follow the directions exactly as they are written. If you are in doubt about any part of the experiment, ask your teacher for assistance.
6. Never perform activities that are not authorized by your teacher. Obtain permission before "experimenting" on your own.
7. Never handle any equipment unless you have specific permission.
8. Take extreme care not to spill any material in the laboratory. If a spill occurs, immediately ask your teacher about the proper cleanup procedure. Never simply pour chemicals or other substances into the sink or trash container.
9. Never eat in the laboratory.
10. Wash your hands before and after each experiment.

First Aid

11. Immediately report all accidents, no matter how minor, to your teacher.
12. Learn what to do in case of specific accidents, such as getting acid in your eyes or on your skin. (Rinse acids from your body with lots of water.)
13. Become aware of the location of the first-aid kit. But your teacher should administer any required first aid due to injury. Or your teacher may send you to the school nurse or call a physician.
14. Know where and how to report an accident or fire. Find out the location of the fire extinguisher, phone, and fire alarm. Keep a list of important phone numbers—such as the fire department and the school nurse —near the phone. Immediately report any fires to your teacher.

Heating and Fire Safety

15. Again, never use a heat source, such as a candle or a burner, without wearing safety goggles.
16. Never heat a chemical you are not instructed to heat. A chemical that is harmless when cool may be dangerous when heated.
17. Maintain a clean work area and keep all materials away from flames.
18. Never reach across a flame.
19. Make sure you know how to light a Bunsen burner. (Your teacher will demonstrate the proper procedure for lighting a burner.) If the flame leaps out of a burner toward you, immediately turn off the gas. Do not touch the burner. It may be hot. And never leave a lighted burner unattended!
20. When heating a test tube or bottle, always point it away from you and others. Chemicals can splash or boil out of a heated test tube.

21. Never heat a liquid in a closed container. The expanding gases produced may blow the container apart, injuring you or others.
22. Before picking up a container that has been heated, first hold the back of your hand near it. If you can feel the heat on the back of your hand, the container may be too hot to handle. Use a clamp or tongs when handling hot containers.

Using Chemicals Safely

23. Never mix chemicals for the "fun of it." You might produce a dangerous, possibly explosive substance.
24. Never touch, taste, or smell a chemical unless you are instructed by your teacher to do so. Many chemicals are poisonous. If you are instructed to note the fumes in an experiment, gently wave your hand over the opening of a container and direct the fumes toward your nose. Do not inhale the fumes directly from the container.
25. Use only those chemicals needed in the activity. Keep all lids closed when a chemical is not being used. Notify your teacher whenever chemicals are spilled.
26. Dispose of all chemicals as instructed by your teacher. To avoid contamination, never return chemicals to their original containers.
27. Be extra careful when working with acids or bases. Pour such chemicals over the sink, not over your workbench.
28. When diluting an acid, pour the acid into water. Never pour water into the acid.
29. Immediately rinse with water any acids that get on your skin or clothing. Then notify your teacher of any acid spill.

Using Glassware Safely

30. Never force glass tubing into a rubber stopper. A turning motion and lubricant will be helpful when inserting glass tubing into rubber stoppers or rubber tubing. Your teacher will demonstrate the proper way to insert glass tubing.
31. Never heat glassware that is not thoroughly dry. Use a wire screen to protect glassware from any flame.
32. Keep in mind that hot glassware will not appear hot. Never pick up glassware without first checking to see if it is hot. See #22.
33. If you are instructed to cut glass tubing, fire-polish the ends immediately to remove sharp edges.
34. Never use broken or chipped glassware. If glassware breaks, notify your teacher and dispose of the glassware in the proper trash container.
35. Never eat or drink from laboratory glassware.
36. Thoroughly clean glassware before putting it away.

Using Sharp Instruments

37. Handle scalpels or razor blades with extreme care. Never cut material toward you; cut away from you.
38. Immediately notify your teacher if you cut your skin when working in the laboratory.

Animal Safety

39. No experiments that cause pain, discomfort, or harm to mammals, birds, reptiles, fish, and amphibians should be done in the classroom or at home.
40. Animals should be handled only if necessary. If an animal is excited or frightened, pregnant, feeding, or with its young, special handling is required.
41. Your teacher will instruct you as to how to handle each animal species that may be brought into the classroom.
42. Clean your hands thoroughly after handling animals or the cage containing animals.

End-of-Experiment Rules

43. After an experiment has been completed, clean up your work area and return all equipment to its proper place.
44. Wash your hands after every experiment.
45. Turn off all candles and burners before leaving the laboratory. Check that the gas line leading to the burner is off as well.

Laboratory Skills Checkup 1 _____

Following Directions

This skills sheet helps reinforce students' appreciation of the need to read all directions before beginning an investigation. Use this skills sheet before your students begin work in the laboratory.

1. Read all of the following directions before you do anything.

2. Print your name, last name first then your first name and middle initial (if you have one), at the top of this page.

3. Draw a line through the word "all" in direction 1.

4. Underline the word "directions" in direction 1.

5. In direction 2, circle the words "your first name."

6. In direction 3, place an "X" in front of the word "through."

7. Cross out the numbers of the even-numbered directions above.

8. In direction 7, cross out the word "above" and write the word "below" above it.

9. Write "Following directions is easy" under your name at the top of this page.

10. In direction 9, add the following sentence after the word "page." "That's what you think!"

11. Draw a square in the upper right-hand corner of this page.

12. Draw a triangle in the lower left-hand corner of this page.

13. Place a circle in the center of the square.

14. Place an "X" in the center of the triangle.

15. Now that you have read all the directions as instructed in direction 1, follow directions 2 and 16 only.

16. Please do not give away what this test is about by saying anything or doing anything to alert your classmates. If you have reached this direction, make believe you are still writing. See how many of your classmates really know how to follow directions.

Laboratory Skills Checkup 2 _____

Defining Elements of a
Scientific Method

Laboratory activities and experiments involve the use of the scientific method. Listed in the left column are the names of parts of this method. The right column contains definitions. Next to each word in the left column, place the letter of the definition that best matches.

Conclusion	F	A. What the person performing the activity sees, hears, smells, or tastes
Control	H	B. Gathering information about the subject of the activity
Data	E	C. Proposed explanation for a problem or observation
Hypothesis	C	D. Factor being tested
Objective	G	E. Measurements
Observation	A	F. Result of a laboratory activity
Research	B	G. Problem that the laboratory activity is designed to solve
Variable	D	H. Experiment with the variable left out

Laboratory Skills Checkup 3 _____

Analyzing Elements of the Scientific Method

Read the following statements and then answer the questions.

1. You have just bought an old-fashioned clock that runs by weights on chains and a pendulum.

2. To get the clock to run, you pull the weights up and start the pendulum swinging. Your watch says 4:00 so you set the clock to this time.

3. Several hours later, you return with a friend to look at your clock. According to your watch it is 8:05, but the clock reads 8:15.

4. After determining that there is nothing wrong with your watch, your friend asks, "What do you think caused the clock to gain time?"

5. You watch the clock for a few minutes and then propose, "I think that if the pendulum swings too quickly, it makes the clock run fast."

6. You continue, "I also think that if the length of the pendulum were increased, the pendulum would swing more slowly and the clock would run on time."

7. "Furthermore," you say, "to test my explanation, I will suspend strings of three different lengths and tie a washer to the end of each. Then, I will swing each length of string from a 45° angle and time how quickly each swings."

Questions

A. In which statement is a **prediction** made? 6 _____

B. Which statement states a **problem**? 4 _____

C. In which statement is an **experiment** described? 7 _____

D. Which statement contains a **hypothesis**? 5 _____

E. Which statements contain **data**? 2, 3, 7 _____

F. Which statement describes **observations**? 3 _____

Laboratory Skills Checkup 4 _____

Performing an Experiment

Read the following statements and then answer the questions.

1. A scientist notices that her pendulum-powered clock is running fast. She wants to find out why.

2. Since the scientist has misplaced the clock's instructions, she goes to the library and reads some books about clocks.

3. The scientist learns that the swinging pendulum controls how quickly the clock hands move. The faster the pendulum swings, the faster the hands go.

4. In light of this information, the scientist guesses that if the pendulum were longer, it would not swing quite as fast.

5. The scientist goes to her laboratory to test her idea. She does the following:

   a. Suspends a string 1 meter long from the ring of a ring stand.
   b. Ties a washer to the end of the string.
   c. Raises the washer to a 45° angle and lets it go.
   d. Records in her notebook the time it takes the washer to make each of the first five swings.
   e. Repeats the procedure using a string 0.50 meter long and 0.25 meter long.

6. The scientist writes in her notebook, "The meter-long pendulum swings two times slower than the 0.25-meter-long pendulum and about one and a half times slower than the 0.50-meter-long pendulum."

7. The scientist finishes her report stating, "It appears that a longer pendulum swings more slowly. Therefore, if I increase the length of the pendulum on my clock, the pendulum will swing more slowly and the clock will not run as fast."

Questions

A. Which statement contains a **conclusion**? 7 _____

B. Which statements refer to **research**? 2, 3 _____

C. Which statement contains a **hypothesis**? 4 _____

D. Which statements describe **observations** being made? 1, 5 _____

E. Which statement describes an **experiment**? 5 _____

F. Which statement **supports** the **hypothesis**? [6] _____

G. In which statement is the **problem** defined? [1] _____

H. Which statements contain **data**? [5, 6] _____

I. What is the **variable** in the experiment? length of the pendulum _____

J. What is the **control** in the experiment? the angle from which the pendulum is swung _____

K. Which statement contains a **generalization**? [7] _____

© Prentice-Hall, Inc.

Laboratory Skills Checkup 5 _____

Identifying Errors

Read the following paragraph and then answer the questions.

Sandy arrived at school and went directly to his physical science class. His teacher gave him a thermometer, a beaker of ice, and a small jar of potassium nitrate, a type of salt. The teacher asked Sandy to determine the amount of salt that would dissolve in 100 mL of water at 5°C. Sandy filled a beaker with 100 mL of water and placed it in the beaker of ice. He cooled the water to 5°C and left the beaker of water in the ice. Sandy next poured some salt onto the pan of the laboratory balance. He measured out 1.5 grams and committed the number to memory. After brushing the salt into his hand, Sandy slowly added it to the water, stirring occasionally with the thermometer. When no more salt would dissolve, he poured the remaining salt back onto the balance pan. By looking at the amount of salt in the pan, Sandy estimated that about 1 gram was left.

Questions

1. Why will Sandy have trouble calculating the amount of potassium nitrate dissolved in the water?

   He did not record the amount of salt he started with, and he may not remember the correct amount.

2. What was wrong with pouring the salt onto the balance pan and his hand? Sandy should have measured the salt on a piece of paper. Some salt could easily be lost when transferring the salt from the balance to Sandy's hand and back onto the balance.

3. What was wrong with Sandy's stirring method? Thermometers break easily and should never be used to stir anything.

4. What mistake did Sandy make when taking the water's temperature? He left the water in the ice after taking the reading. By the time Sandy finished the experiment the water would be colder than 5°C.

5. What was wrong with Sandy's final measurement of the amount of salt?

   Instead of measuring the amount by balancing the scale, Sandy just looked at the amount of salt. Also, an estimate should not be used in an investigation that involves making measurements to determine a precise amount.

Laboratory Skills Checkup 6

Making Measurements

Look at the drawings and write the letter of the drawing next to the description that it matches.

1. Measures time ^D_____

2. Measures weight ^G_____

3. Measures mass ^H_____

4. Measures volume ^A_____

5. Measures air pressure ^F_____

6. Measures temperature ^B_____

7. Measures length ^C_____

8. Measures electric current ^E_____

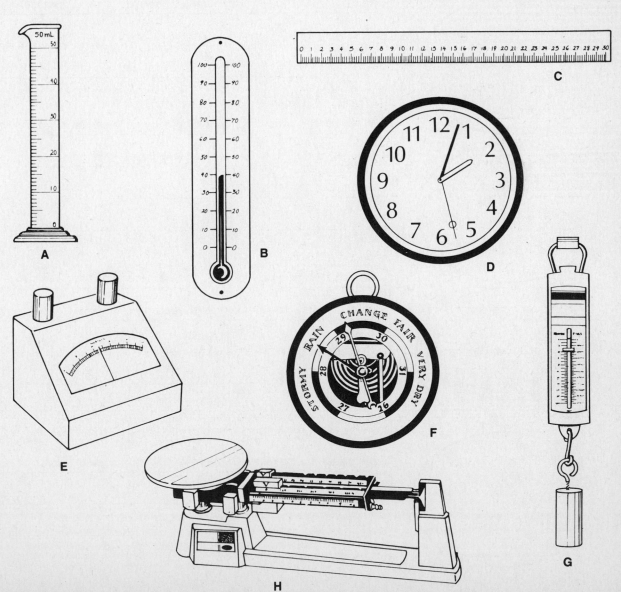

Laboratory Skills Checkup 7 ——————————————

Safety First

Circle any drawing that shows an unsafe laboratory activity and explain why it is unsafe.

Safety goggles should always be worn whenever a person is

working with chemicals, burners, or any substance that might get

into the eyes.

_____

_____

Never smell the contents of a test tube or other apparatus directly.

Use your hand to wave the fumes toward you from a distance.

_____

_____

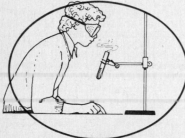

When heating a test tube, always point its open end away from

yourself or others. Wear heat-resistant gloves when holding a

heated object.

_____

_____

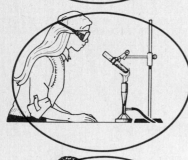

Never heat a liquid in a closed container. The expanding gases

produced may blow the container apart.

_____

_____

Never eat or drink from laboratory glassware. The last material in

the glassware may have been poisonous and traces of it may still be

in the glassware.

_____

_____

_____ *Laboratory Investigation* _____

Chapter 1   Exploring Physical Science

1

Metric Measurement: Volume and Temperature

You may want to refer students to pages 28–29 in their textbook for a general discussion of the measurements of volume and temperature.

Time required: 40 minutes

Background Information

The amount of space an object takes up is called its volume. The basic unit of volume is the liter (L). Smaller volumes are measured in milliliters (mL), or 1/1000 of a liter. In the laboratory, the graduated cylinder is used to measure the volume of liquids.

Temperature is measured with a thermometer. The unit of measurement for temperature is degrees Celsius (°C).

In this investigation you will learn how to accurately measure the volume and temperature of a liquid.

Problem

How can you accurately measure the volume and temperature of a liquid?

Materials *(per group)*

water
2 100-mL beakers
100-mL graduated cylinder
glass-marking pencil
2 Celsius thermometers
ice cubes

Procedure
Part A   Measuring the Volume of a Liquid

1. Fill a beaker half full of water.

2. Pour the water in the beaker into the graduated cylinder.

3. Measure the amount of water in the graduated cylinder. To accurately measure the volume, your eye must be at the same level as the bottom of the meniscus. The meniscus is the curved surface of a column of liquid. See Figure 1.

4. Record the volume of water to the nearest mL in Data Table 1.

5. Repeat steps 1 through 4 with a beaker that is one fourth full of water.

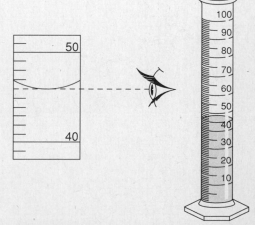

Figure 1

© Prentice-Hall, Inc.

Part B Measuring the Temperature of a Liquid

🧪 **1.** With the glass-marking pencil, label the beakers A and B.

2. Fill both beakers with 50 mL of water. Record this volume in Data Table 2.

3. Place a thermometer in each beaker. Record the temperature of the water in each beaker in Data Table 3.

Be sure that you tell students not to stir the water in the beaker with the thermometer.

4. Carefully add three ice cubes to the water in beaker B.

5. After one minute, observe the temperature of the water in each beaker. Record the temperatures in Data Table 3.

6. After five minutes, observe the temperature of the water in each beaker. Record the temperatures in Data Table 3.

7. Find the volume of the water in beaker A. Record the volume in Data Table 2.

8. After the ice in beaker B has melted, find the volume of water. Record the volume in Data Table 2.

Observations

DATA TABLE 1

	Volume of Water (mL)
One half filled beaker	Answers will vary.
One fourth filled beaker	

DATA TABLE 2

	Volume of Water (mL)	
	Beginning of Investigation	End of Investigation
Beaker A	Answers will vary.	
Beaker B		

DATA TABLE 3

	Temperature of Water (°C)		
	Beginning of Investigation	After 1 Minute	After 5 Minutes
Beaker A		Answers will vary.	
Beaker B			

18

Analysis and Conclusions

1. What is the largest volume of a liquid that your graduated cylinder is able to measure?

   100 mL

2. What is the smallest volume of a liquid that your graduated cylinder is able to measure?

   1 mL

3. Did the temperature of the water in beakers A and B change during the investigation?

   Explain. After the ice cubes were added to the water in beaker B, the temperature of the water

   decreased.

4. Was there a difference in the volume of water in the beakers at the end of the

   investigation? Explain. The volume of water in beaker B increased because the melted ice added

   more water to the existing 50 mL of water.

Critical Thinking and Application

1. Of the following graduated cylinders, 100 mL, 25 mL, or 10 mL, which would you use to

   accurately measure 8 mL of a liquid? Explain. To measure 8 mL of a liquid, it is best to use a 10

   mL graduated cylinder because it has finer graduations and thus provides for a more accurate

   measurement.

© Prentice-Hall, Inc.

2. Using a Celsius thermometer, how would you determine the temperature of your classroom? Carefully suspend the Celsius thermometer from its top so that it does not come in contact with any other objects. Then read the temperature after a few minutes.

3. When ice was added to beaker B, the thermometer was not removed. Explain why. The removal of the thermometer from beaker B would expose it to the air temperature of the room, thus introducing a new variable and affecting the data.

4. Suppose the water in beaker B had been stirred after the ice had been added. What would be the immediate effect of this on the temperature of the water? Would stirring have an effect on the final temperature of the water? The immediate effect might have been a *faster* decrease in temperature, as the removal of heat energy and subsequent temperature drop would have reached the thermometer bulb faster. But this would have no effect on the final temperature of the water.

5. Why do you think the water in the graduated cylinder forms a meniscus? The water is attracted (adheres) to the sides of the graduated cylinder. As a result, the water forms a curved surface at the top.

Going Further

Evaporation is sometimes described as a cooling process. This is because as a liquid evaporates it takes heat from the surroundings. Using water, two Celsius thermometers, a small piece of gauze, and some thread, design an investigation to test the statement. Indicate the control and the variable. Include problem, hypothesis, procedure, observations, and conclusions. With your teacher's permission, perform this investigation.

_____ *Laboratory Investigation* _____

Tools of the Scientist: The Bunsen Burner and a Filtering Apparatus

You may want to refer students to pages 26–29 in their textbook for a general discussion of tools of the scientist.

Time required: Part A—15 minutes
Part B—30 minutes

Part A   Using the Bunsen Burner
Background Information

Often a chemist needs to heat materials in a laboratory. One of the most efficient ways to do this is to use a Bunsen burner. Bunsen burners are made in a variety of designs. In every one, however, the burner functions by the combustion of a mixture of air and gas. In most burners, the amounts of air and gas can be controlled. In some situations, portable liquid-petroleum burners are used instead of Bunsen burners. Electric hot plates may be used as well.

In this investigation you will learn the parts of the Bunsen burner and their functions. You will also learn how to use the burner safely in the laboratory.

Problem

How can the Bunsen burner be safely used to heat materials in the laboratory?

Materials (*per group*)

Bunsen burner or portable   beaker tongs
   liquid-petroleum burner   iron ring
ring stand   safety goggles
2 250-mL beakers   100-mL graduated cylinder
wire gauze

Procedure

1. Examine your burner when it is not connected to the gas outlet. If your burner is the type that can easily be taken apart, unscrew the barrel from the base and locate the parts shown in Figure 1. If you are using a portable liquid-petroleum burner, see Figure 2. As you examine the parts, think about their functions.

   The **barrel** is the area where the air and gas mix.
   The **collar** can be turned to adjust the intake of air. If you turn the collar so that the holes are larger, more air will be drawn into the barrel.
   The **air intake openings** are the holes in the collar through which the air is drawn.
   The **base** supports the burner so that it does not tip over.
   The **gas intake tube** brings the supply of gas from the outlet to the burner.
   The **spud** is the small opening through which the gas flows. The small opening causes the gas to enter the barrel with great speed.

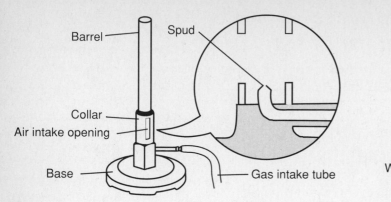

Barrel Spud

Collar
Air intake opening

Base   Gas intake tube

Figure 1

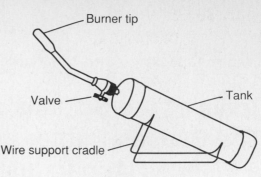

Burner tip

Valve   Tank

Wire support cradle

Figure 2

 2. Reassemble the Bunsen burner if necessary and connect the tube to the gas outlet. Put on safety goggles. Make sure that the burner is away from all flammable materials.

3. Adjust the collar so that the air intake openings are half open. Hold a lighted match about 2 cm above and just to the right of the barrel. Hold the match in this position while you open the gas valve slowly until it is fully open. The burner can be turned off by using the valve. Do not lean over the burner when lighting it.

4. Practice relighting the burner several times. Adjust the collar so that the flame is blue and a pale blue inner cone is visible.

5. Adjust the flow of gas until the flame is about 6 cm high. Some burners have a valve in the base to regulate the flow of gas, but the flow of gas can always be adjusted at the gas outlet valve. After adjusting the flow of gas, shut off the burner. Leave your safety goggles on as you proceed with step 6.

6. Arrange the apparatus as pictured in Figure 3.

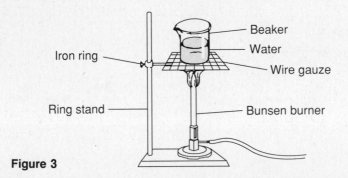

Iron ring

Ring stand

Beaker
Water
Wire gauze

Bunsen burner

Figure 3

7. Adjust the iron ring so that the bottom of the beaker is about 2 cm above the mouth of the barrel. Measure 100 mL of water in the graduated cylinder and pour it into the beaker.

8. Light the burner and heat the beaker. The bottom of the beaker should just be touching the top of the inner cone of the flame. Record the time it takes for the water to start boiling rapidly. Using the tongs, carefully remove the beaker.

9. Repeat the procedure with the other beaker at a height of about 6 cm above the mouth of the barrel. Record the time it takes for the water to start boiling rapidly at this height. Be sure that the starting temperature of the water is the same in each trial.
In steps 8 and 9, caution students to ignore the appearance of small bubbles of oxygen gas and wait until rapid boiling begins.

Observations

DATA TABLE

Height Above Burner (cm)	Time to Boil (min)
2	
6	

Analysis and Conclusions

1. What would happen if the air intake openings were made very small?

   The gas would not burn as well. The flame would become yellow. The flame would not be as hot.

2. If the burner did not light even after the gas outlet valve was open, what might be wrong? The spud might be clogged.

3. Where is the hottest part of the flame? Where did the water boil the soonest?

   At a point just above the inner blue cone.

4. Why is it important to make sure that the volume of water and the starting temperature are the same in each trial?

   The amount of heat given off by the flame must be the only variable.

Part B Filtering
Background Information

Physical scientists are able to separate materials based on their differing properties. One of the techniques used quite often is filtering. In this activity you will learn how to separate a salt-and-sand mixture by adding water and filtering the mixture. The salt will be reclaimed.

Problem

How can a salt-and-sand mixture be separated?

Materials (*per group*)

Bunsen burner or portable liquid petroleum burner	ring stand	wire gauze
	safety goggles	evaporating dish
	glass stirring rod	tongs
filter paper	2 250-mL beakers	10 g salt-and-sand mixture
funnel	small iron ring	graduated cylinder

© Prentice-Hall, Inc.

Procedure

1. Obtain a 10 g sample of salt-and-sand mixture from your teacher.

2. Add 50 mL of water to the salt-and-sand mixture in the beaker. Stir.

3. Prepare filter paper as shown in Figure 4. Fold a circle of filter paper across the middle. Fold the resulting half-circle to form a quarter-circle. Open the folded paper into a cone, leaving a triple layer on one side and a single layer on the other.

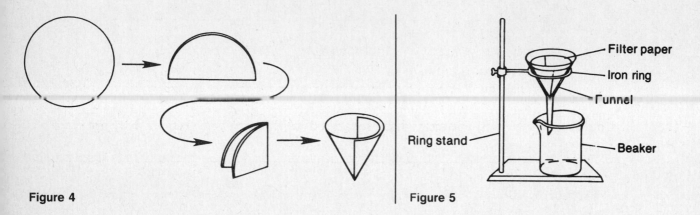

Figure 4

Figure 5

4. Support a glass funnel as shown in Figure 5. Place the cone of the filter paper in the funnel and wet the paper so that it adheres smoothly to the walls of the funnel. Set a clean beaker beneath the funnel in such a way that the stem of the funnel touches the side of the beaker. Funnel-stem placement is to prevent the liquid from splashing as it filters into the beaker.

5. Pour the salt-sand-water mixture slowly into the funnel. Do not let the mixture overflow the filter paper.

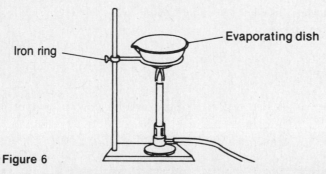

Figure 6

If time is short, it isn't necessary to wait for all of the mixture to be filtered. Set a time limit for your students and evaporate whatever filters through in that time.

6. Carefully remove the filter paper from the funnel and dispose of it in the waste container provided by your teacher. Do not throw sand or filter paper in the sink.

7. Set up the evaporating dish and equipment as shown in Figure 6.

8. Pour some of the contents of the beaker into the evaporating dish. Put on your safety goggles. Heat the contents carefully. Do not let the solution boil over or spatter onto the table top. Turn off the burner when nearly all the liquid has evaporated. The remainder of the water will be evaporated by the heat from the dish.

Observations

When all the water has evaporated, what remains in the evaporating dish?

A white solid substance remains in the evaporating dish.

Analysis and Conclusions

1. What is the probable identity of the substance left in the evaporating dish?

   Salt.

2. Could a mixture of sugar and salt be separated in the same way? Why or why not?

   No. Both sugar and salt are soluble in water.

3. The material left in the filter paper is called the residue. If a mixture of chalk dust, salt, and water were poured through filter paper, what would the residue be?

   The chalk dust.

4. Could two liquids such as alcohol and water be separated this way? Why or why not?

   No. Both would pass through the filter paper.

Critical Thinking and Application

1. A student heated a beaker containing a liquid over a yellow flame. After the beaker was removed, the student noticed a black deposit on the underside of the beaker.

   a. Where did the black deposit come from? The black soot comes from the incomplete burning of

   the gas.

   b. What could the student do the next time to avoid having the black deposit?

   Make sure enough air is admitted so that the flame burns with a blue, not yellow, color.

2. State two reasons why a blue flame is preferred over a yellow flame in a Bunsen burner.

   A blue flame burns hotter and cleaner than a yellow flame.

3. What safety precautions should be followed before lighting a burner?

Put on safety goggles; tie back long hair and loose clothing; know the locations of the fire extinguishers

and fire blankets and how to use them.

4. In what situation should the filter paper not be wet with water to make it adhere to the

sides of the funnel? Why? When the liquid being filtered does not mix with water, the liquid will not be

able to pass through the filter paper if it is wet with water.

Going Further

Test the ability of different kinds of laboratory burners to heat water to boiling. Determine if there is a difference in the efficiency with which different burners are able to heat objects.

_____ *Laboratory Investigation* _____

Chapter 2   General Properties of Matter _____ **3** _____

Determining Density

You may want to refer students to pages 49–54 in their textbook for a general discussion of density.

Time required: Part A—10 minutes
Part B—20 minutes

Background Information

Which is heavier, a kilogram of lead or a kilogram of feathers? This is an old question with a simple answer. Since both objects have a mass of 1 kg, they are equally heavy. Each feather, however, has less mass than each piece of lead. So a greater number of feathers is needed to make a kilogram. And the more feathers there are, the more space they take up. The space an object occupies is its volume. So a kilogram of feathers has a greater volume than a kilogram of lead. The mass of a certain volume of feathers is different from the mass of the same volume of lead.

The mass of a specific volume of an object is called density. Density can be expressed mathematically as:

$$\text{Density} = \frac{\text{Mass}}{\text{Volume}}$$

Density is a property of all objects. In this investigation you will learn about this important characteristic.

Problem

How can the density of an object be determined?

Materials *(per group)*

triple-beam balance   A standard density kit is helpful here. It contains all the materials listed.
metric ruler
100-mL graduated cylinder
2 rectangular solids of the same
   material but of different
   dimensions, such as a bar and
   a cube of iron, copper, or
   aluminum
1 large piece of modeling clay   Total mass should not exceed 125 g.

Procedure
Part A   Density of Rectangular Solids

1. Using the balance, determine the mass of each solid. Follow the directions given by your teacher for the proper use of the balance. Read the mass of each solid to the nearest 0.1 g. Record your data in the appropriate column of Data Table 1.

2. Determine the volume of each solid using the metric ruler to measure length, width, and height. Read these values to the nearest 0.1 cm. Now use the formula for volume $V = L \times W \times H$, where L = length, W = width, and H = height, to calculate the volume of each solid. Add these data to Data Table 1.

3. Calculate the density of each sample, using the formula Density = Mass/Volume ($D = M/V$), and record your results in Data Table 1.

Part B   Density of Irregular Solids

1. Separate the large piece of modeling clay into five pieces of different sizes. Make sure that the mass of the smallest sample is no less than 5 g.   Emphasize to students that pieces must be of different sizes.

2. Using the balance, determine the mass of each sample to the nearest 0.1 g. Record your data in the appropriate column of Data Table 2.

3. The volume of an irregular solid cannot be determined in the same way as a rectangular solid, since length, width, and height cannot be accurately measured. However, the volume of an irregular solid can be measured by the displacement of water.

4. Place some water in the graduated cylinder and read its volume to the nearest 0.1 mL. Carefully add a sample of clay, making sure you do not let any water splash out of the graduated cylinder. Read the new volume to the nearest 0.1 mL. Subtract the original volume from the new volume. This volume of displaced water is equal to the volume of the clay sample. Record this value in Data Table 2.
Explain to students that using a graduated cylinder gives volume measurements in mL. However, for water 1mL = 1cm³, so either unit can be used. The Data Table and graph units used are cm³.

5. Repeat the procedure for the other four samples of clay. Record your data in Data Table 2.

6. Using the mass and volume values in Data Table 2, construct a graph that illustrates the relationship between mass and volume of each sample. Use the vertical axis for mass and the horizontal axis for volume.
Help students select a proper scale for mass and volume.

7. Connect the five points on the graph and extend the line to the zero point. The line should be a straight one connecting as many points as possible.
Students will need some help with this. The overhead projector is useful here. Show students how to continue the line so that additional values can be extrapolated. They will need to extrapolate to answer question 4 in Conclusions.

Observations
Part A

DATA TABLE 1   Emphasize units for density, g/cm³.

Description of Object	Material (if Known)	Mass (g)	Volume (cm³)	Density (g/cm³)
Bar	Iron Copper Aluminum	Varies	Varies	7.9 8.9 2.7
Cube	Iron Copper Aluminum	Varies	Varies	7.9 8.9 2.7

Part B

DATA TABLE 2

Clay	Mass (g)	Volume (cm³)
Sample 1		
Sample 2		
Sample 3	Values vary.	
Sample 4		
Sample 5		

Analysis and Conclusions

1. How do the densities of your two samples compare? Explain your observation.

   The two samples have the same densities even though they have different masses and volumes. Both

   samples are made of the same material, and all materials have a characteristic density.

2. What is the volume of a solid whose dimensions are 1.0 cm × 6.0 cm × 2.0 cm? Remember to include the proper units. 1.0 cm × 6.0 cm × 2.0 cm = 12.0 cm³

3. If the mass of the object in question 2 is 60 g, what is its density?

   60 g/12 cm³ = 5 g/cm³

4. Using your graph, determine the volume of a sample of clay that has a mass of 160 g.

   100 cm³

5. Using your graph, determine the density of a piece of clay that has a volume of 3 cm³.

   All samples will have the same density.   1.6   g/cm³

6. Using your graph (or data from your data table), determine the density of a piece of clay that has a mass of 25 g. 1.6 _____ g/cm³

© Prentice-Hall, Inc.

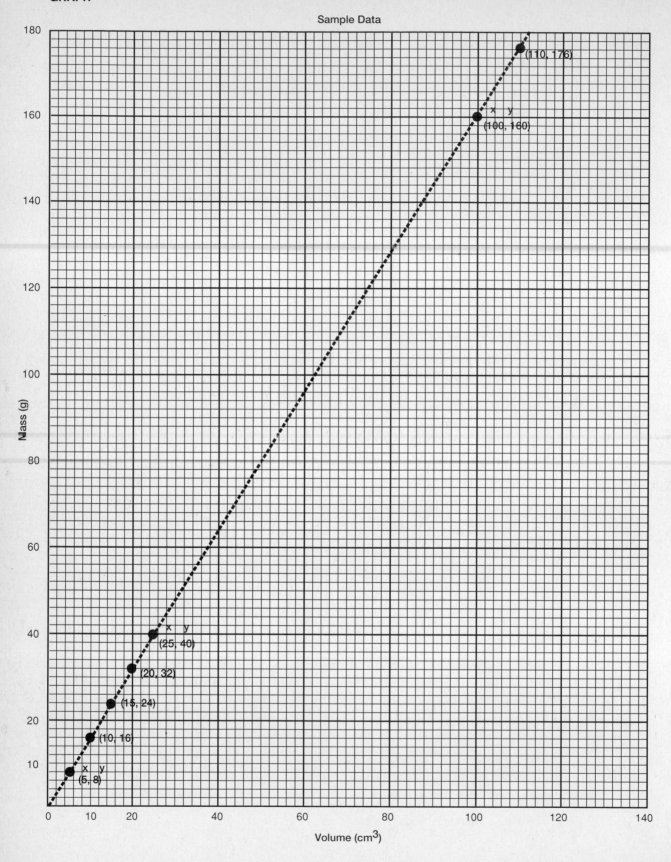

Sample Data

Critical Thinking and Application

1. Could the water displacement method be used to determine the volume of a rectangular solid as well as an irregular solid? <u>Yes.</u> Explain. _____

   The volume of water displaced is equal to the volume of the object whether it is a rectangular (regular)

   solid or an irregular solid.

2. If an object with a density of 5g/cm³ is cut into two equal pieces, what is the density of each piece?

   5 g/cm³. Density is not affected by size or shape.

3. The diagrams below represent three samples of the same substance, each having a different size and shape. Arrange the letters of the samples to show the order by volume from largest to smallest. <u>C, A, B</u>

   What is the density of A? <u>3 g/cm³</u> B? <u>3 g/cm³</u> C? <u>3 g/cm³</u>

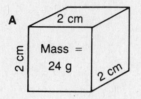
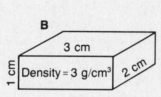
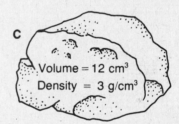

4. Explain how the results of this laboratory investigation show that differences in size and shape do not affect the density of a given substance.

   Both the bar and the cube of iron, copper, or aluminum have the same density regardless of shape. The

   five samples of clay have the same density regardless of size.

5. Why is density such an important physical property?

   Every substance has a characteristic density, so density can be used to identify an unknown substance.

   Also, because density is mass per unit volume, substances can be compared to one another

   accurately.

Going Further

1. The density of water is 1 g/cm^3. An object will float in water if its density is less than 1 g/cm^3. If its density is greater than 1 g/cm^3, the object will sink. Given the following substances and their densities, determine whether each substance will float or sink in water.

aluminum 2.7 g/cm^3 __S__   gold   19.3 g/cm^3 __S__   chlorine   3.2 g/cm^3 __S__

arsenic   5.7 g/cm^3 __S__   neon   0.89 g/cm^3 __F__   uranium 19.0 g/cm^3 __S__

helium   0.18 g/cm^3 __F__   lithium 0.53 g/cm^3 __F__   potassium 0.86 g/cm^3 __F__

2. Substance X has a volume of 50 cm^3 and a mass of 160 g. Will substance X float or sink?

160 g/50 cm^3 = 3.2 g/cm^3; sink

Substance Y has a volume of 140 cm^3 and a mass of 112 g. Will substance Y float or sink?

112 g/140 cm^3 = 0.8 g/cm^3; float

_____ *Laboratory Investigation* _____

4

Determining the Density of Liquids

You may want to refer students to pages 49–54 in their textbook for a general discussion of density.

Time required: 40 minutes

Background Information

In the text you learned that mass and volume are general properties of all matter. Density is the ratio of mass to volume. The particular density of a specific kind of matter helps to identify it and distinguish it from other kinds of matter. Liquids have density, and it is possible to determine their densities in grams per milliliter (g/mL).

In this investigation you will determine the density of several liquids by measuring their mass and volume. You will also learn how to calculate the density of liquids by using a wood float.

Problem

How can you determine the density of liquids?

Materials *(per group)*

4 100-mL graduated cylinders
wooden cylinder about 10 cm
  long (A small pencil or thin
  dowel works well.)
laboratory balance
50 mL ethyl alcohol

oil (salad type)
salt water (several samples of
  different concentrations—
  A, B, C)
wax marking pencil

Premeasure 50 mL of oil in 3 or 4 graduates and have groups share these to minimize cleanup.

To prepare these solutions, add each of the following amounts of NaCl to 1L of water: 25 g, 50 g, and 100 g.

Procedure

🔺 **1.** Place the empty graduated cylinder on the laboratory balance. Record the mass in the Data Table.

2. Pour 50 mL of water into the graduated cylinder. Find the mass of the graduated cylinder and the water. Record this mass in the Data Table. Calculate the mass of the water by subtracting the mass of the empty graduated cylinder from the mass of the graduated cylinder with water. Record your answer in the Data Table. Keep the water in the cylinder for use in step 5.

3. Calculate the density of water by dividing the mass of the water by the volume.

$$\text{Density} = \frac{\text{Mass}}{\text{Volume}}$$

👁 **4.** Using three other graduated cylinders, repeat steps 2 and 3 first using alcohol, then one
✚   of the samples of salt water, and then oil. Keep the liquids in the cylinders for use in
    step 5.   Have the students use the 100 g salt/L of water sample.

5. Carefully place the wooden cylinder in each liquid in the graduated cylinders, one at a time. See Figure 1. Note the level of the wooden cylinder in the water, the alcohol, the salt water, and the oil. In which liquid does the wooden cylinder float highest? In which liquid does the wooden cylinder float lowest?

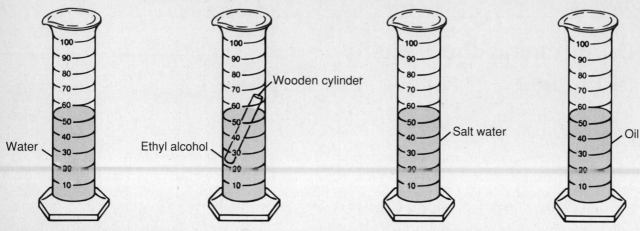

Figure 1

6. Use the wooden cylinder to test the remaining samples of salt water. With a wax marking pencil, mark the float levels of the salt water on your wooden cylinder.

Observations

DATA TABLE

Liquid	Mass of Empty Graduate (g)	Mass of Graduate and Liquid (g)	Mass of Liquid (g)	Volume of Liquid (mL)	Density of Liquid (g/mL)
Water				50	
Alcohol				50	
Salt water				50	
Oil				50	

Analysis and Conclusions

1. Which sample of salt water was the most dense? How did you know?

Answers will vary depending upon the concentration of salt used. The wooden cylinder would float

highest in the densest or most concentrated sample.

2. List the four liquids you used in this experiment in order of increasing density.

Alcohol, oil, water, salt water.

Critical Thinking and Application

1. Which has the greater mass, 1 L of water or 1 L of alcohol? Why?

   1 L of water, because it is more dense.

2. Which takes up a greater volume, 1000 g of water or 1000 g of alcohol? Why?

   1000 g of alcohol, because it is less dense and a given volume would weigh less than an equal volume of

   water. A given mass of alcohol would take up a greater volume than an equal mass of water.

3. Which is more dense, 1 mL of water or 50 L of water? Why?

   They have equal density because the density of water is a property that does not change, regardless of

   the quantity of water.

4. Predict what would happen if all the liquids used in this lab were poured into one beaker.

   The liquids would form layers; from bottom to top they would be salt water, water, oil, and alcohol.

Going Further

   Determine the density of each sample of salt water used in this investigation. Describe the method you used. Construct a table of your results.

© Prentice-Hall, Inc.

Laboratory Investigation

Chapter 2   General Properties of Matter

5

Determining Specific Gravity

You may want to refer students to pages 49–54 in their textbook for a general discussion of density.

Time required: 35 minutes

Background Information

One of the physical properties of matter that may be used to identify it is its specific gravity. Specific gravity is a comparison between the density of a substance and the density of pure water. Since the density of pure water is 1.0 g/mL, a substance with a specific gravity of 3.5, for example, would be 3.5 times denser than water.

In this investigation you will determine the specific gravity of several different substances by finding the mass of each and comparing it to the mass of the same volume of water.

Problem

How can an object's specific gravity be determined?

Materials *(per student or per group)*

mineral sample
rock sample
rubber stopper
cork
triple-beam balance
overflow can
250-mL beaker

Procedure

1. Find the mass of the empty, dry beaker. Record the mass in the Data Table.

2. Find the mass of the first object. Record the mass in the Data Table.

3. Fill the overflow can with water so that the water is above the spout. Allow the excess water to spill out into the sink.

4. Carefully drop the object into the overflow can and catch the displaced water in the beaker. If the object floats, push it down with a pencil or pen so that it is completely under water.

5. Find the mass of the beaker plus the water. Calculate the mass of the water alone and record it in the Data Table.

6. Calculate the specific gravity of the object according to the following ratio:

$$\text{Specific gravity} = \frac{\text{Mass of object}}{\text{Mass of displaced water}}$$

7. Repeat steps 1 through 6 for each additional object.

Observations

DATA TABLE

Object	Mass of Beaker	Mass of Water and Beaker	Mass of Displaced Water	Mass of Object	Specific Gravity

Analysis and Conclusions

1. When the object is placed in the overflow can, it displaces a certain volume of water. How does the volume of displaced water compare to the volume of the object?

They are the same.

2. What is the relationship between specific gravity and density?

Specific gravity compares the density of an object to the density of water.

3. If the object floats in water, why is it necessary to submerge it to obtain accurate results? The object must be completely submerged so that the water it displaces is the same as its volume.

Critical Thinking and Application

1. Explain why the specific gravity of certain objects, such as table salt, cannot be determined by the method used in this investigation.

Because it dissolves in water, you would not be able to determine its volume by water displacement.

2. If two objects have the same specific gravity, does it mean that they are made of the same kind of matter? Explain. No; two different objects or substances may have the same specific gravity. Other properties would be different, however, and allow you to distinguish between them.

_____

_____

3. How could you use specific gravity to help you find out if a piece of gold jewelry is made of real gold or some other substance? Consult reference books to find the specific gravity of gold (or 14k gold) as well as of other metals that might be in the jewelry. Determine the specific gravity of the jewelry and see which of your "known" metals has a nearly similar specific gravity.

_____

_____

_____

_____

Going Further

This is not the only method of finding specific gravity. Use reference books to find out about other methods that may be used to determine specific gravity.

Laboratory Investigation

Chapter 3   Physical and Chemical Changes

6

Investigating Phase Changes

You may want to refer students to pages 69–75 in their textbook for a general discussion of phase changes.

Time required: Part A—25 minutes
Part B—25 minutes

Background Information

Pure matter can exist in three phases: solid, liquid, and gas. A phase change occurs when matter changes from one phase to another. Phase changes occur when heat is added or removed from a substance. The melting point of a substance is the temperature at which the solid-liquid phase change takes place. The freezing point is the temperature at which the liquid-solid phase change takes place. Notice that the melting point of a substance is the same as its freezing point. At this temperature, solid and liquid can exist together.

In Part A of this investigation you will observe what happens when the compound paradichlorobenzene (PDB) is cooled from a liquid to a solid, or freezes. In Part B the procedure will be reversed, and the solid will be heated until the substance melts and reaches a temperature above its melting point. The data obtained from Parts A and B will be used to construct a graph.

Problem

What temperature changes occur when a substance changes phase?

Materials *(per group)*

4 g paradichlorobenzene crystals
test tube
Celsius thermometer
hot plate
test-tube holder or clamp
2 400-mL beakers
safety goggles
heat-resistant gloves
test-tube rack
colored pencils
glass-marking pencil

PDB is used as moth-repellant flakes and is easily obtainable in most supermarkets.

Procedure
Part A

To save time, begin heating water before class if possible, or have students begin heating water as soon as class begins.

1. Half fill the two beakers with water. Heat one of the beakers on the hot plate until the temperature of the water is about 90°C. Do not boil the water.

2. Obtain a test tube of PDB crystals and place it in the beaker of hot water. Allow the PDB to melt completely. As soon as it is melted, insert a thermometer in it and record the temperature. See Figure 1.

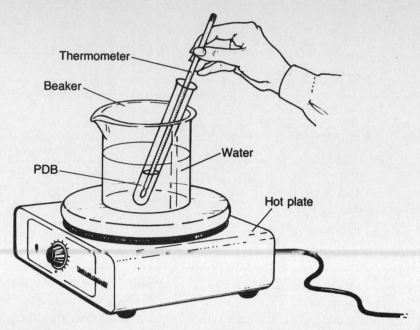

Figure 1

Caution students that if the thermometer bulb rests against the glass, it will be cooled and will indicate a lower temperature. You may want to insert the thermometers into 1-hole rubber stoppers ahead of time (do not let students do this) and have students clamp the thermometers in place using a ring stand and clamp.

3. Remove the test tube from the beaker and place it in the beaker of cool water. Hold the thermometer in the PDB so that it does not touch the sides of the test tube, and record the temperature every 30 seconds in Data Table 1. Between readings, stir the PDB constantly until it becomes solid. Be sure to note in your data when the liquid PDB first starts to solidify and when there is no liquid PDB left. Continue to record the temperature until it drops to 40°C.

4. Note what happens to the volume of liquid PDB as it turns into solid PDB.

Part B

5. Be sure the beaker of water on the hot plate is still heated as in step 1. Place the test tube with solid PDB in the beaker of hot water. Record the temperature of PDB in Data Table 2 as soon as you place it in the hot water. Read and record the temperature every 30 seconds until solid PDB has changed completely to liquid.

6. When the thermometer is able to move, use it to stir the mixture of solid-liquid PDB. Continue stirring and recording the temperature every 30 seconds until the temperature of the sample reaches 60°C. Note in your data when the solid PDB begins to melt and when it has completely melted.

7. Remove the thermometer and wipe it clean. Remove the test tube from the hot water and allow it to cool in the test-tube rack before replacing the cork and returning it to your teacher.

8. Graph your data on Graph 1. Use one color for the data you obtained while cooling the PDB and another color for the data you obtained while heating the PDB. Provide a key to indicate what each color represents.

Observations

DATA TABLE 1 (Cooling Curve)

Time (min)	Temperature (°C)	Time (min)	Temperature (°C)
½		7½	
1		8	
1½		8½	
2		9	
2½		9½	
3		10	
3½		10½	
4		11	
4½		11½	
5		12	
5½		12½	
6		13	
6½		13½	
7		14	

DATA TABLE 2 (Heating Curve)

Time (min)	Temperature (°C)	Time (min)	Temperature (°C)
½		7½	
1		8	
1½		8½	
2		9	
2½		9½	
3		10	
3½		10½	
4		11	
4½		11½	
5		12	
5½		12½	
6		13	
6½		13½	
7		14	

© Prentice-Hall, Inc.

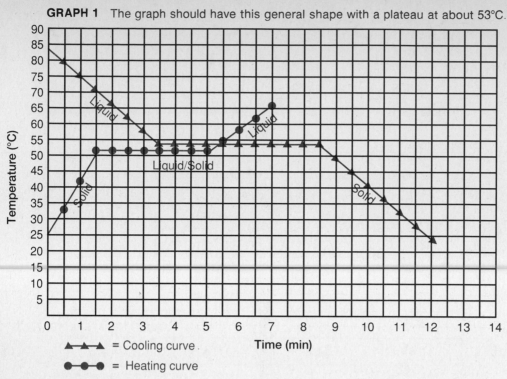

GRAPH 1 The graph should have this general shape with a plateau at about 53°C.

(Graph: Temperature (°C) on y-axis from 5 to 90, Time (min) on x-axis from 0 to 14)

Labels on graph: Liquid, Solid, Liquid/Solid, Liquid, Solid

▲—▲—▲ = Cooling curve
●—●—● = Heating curve

Analysis and Conclusions

1. At what temperature does PDB become solid? __53°C__ How does this compare to the temperature at which solid PDB become a liquid? __It is the same—53°C.__

2. Looking at the slopes of the lines on your graph, how many different sections make up your graph? __3__

3. Describe what occurs in the section on your graph where the line is horizontal.
   The PDB is changing phase and no temperature change is occurring.

4. What happened to the volume of PDB as it became a solid?
   It decreased.

   What does this indicate about the density of solid PDB as compared to liquid PDB?
   Solid PDB is denser.

44

Critical Thinking and Application

1. As the PDB was melting, heat was being added to it but the temperature did not rise. Where did the heat energy go? The energy made the molecules move farther apart.

_____

2. If you used ice instead of PDB in this experiment, how do you think your results would be different? The curves would be similar, but the temperatures would be different. Also, the volume of solid water would be greater than liquid water.

_____

_____

_____

_____

_____

_____

3. If you used twice as much PDB, how would your results be different? Explain. The melting point/freezing point would be the same because this is determined by the nature of the substance. However, it would take longer to heat and cool because there is twice as much mass.

_____

_____

_____

_____

4. A student wanted to solve the problem: "Which freezes fastest, hot water or cold water?" Using the scientific method, describe an experiment the student might do to find the answer. Answers will vary.

_____

_____

_____

_____

_____

_____

What would your hypothesis be if you were doing this experiment?

Answers will vary. Students should realize that cold water freezes faster.

_____

_____

_____

Going Further

Do the experiment you have described in answer to question 4. Record your observations and conclusions.

_____ *Laboratory Investigation* _____

Chapter 3 Physical and Chemical Changes

7

Physical and Chemical Changes

You may want to refer students to pages 62–78 in their textbook for a general discussion of physical and chemical changes.

Time required: 45 minutes

Background Information

Matter is constantly changing. The two kinds of changes that occur in matter are physical and chemical changes. In a physical change, no new substances are formed. However, physical properties such as size, shape, color, or phase may change. Dissolving, melting, evaporating, and grinding are examples of physical change.

As a result of chemical change, one or more "new" substances with new and different properties are formed. The new substances are different from the original substance. Burning and the rusting of iron are examples of chemical change.

In this investigation you will observe physical and chemical changes and learn to recognize each type of change when it occurs.

Problem

What are the differences between physical and chemical changes?

Materials *(per student)*

birthday candle
aluminum foil (15 cm × 15 cm)
modeling clay
small piece of paper
watch glass
Bunsen burner
scoop
magnesium ribbon (1 cm long)
1 M hydrochloric acid   To prepare: Add 86 mL 12 M HCl per
safety goggles   liter of solution. Prepare ahead and use
2 test tubes   dropper bottles for storage.
test-tube rack
test-tube clamp
insulating pad
matches
table salt
dropper bottle of 0.1 M silver   AgNO₃ may be purchased at this
   nitrate   concentration. Store it in brown dropper
                                   bottles.

Procedure

 1. Take a small piece of modeling clay and place it on the square of aluminum foil. Firmly place a candle in the clay so that it is well supported. Light the candle and allow it to burn while you continue with the rest of the investigation. Record your observations of the burning candle in the space provided in Observations.

© Prentice-Hall, Inc.

2. Tear the piece of paper into small pieces and place them on the watch glass. Place the watch glass and pieces of paper on the insulating pad. Light the pieces of paper with a match and allow them to burn completely. Record your observations of the burning paper.

3. Add a small scoop of table salt to a test tube that has been half-filled with tap water. Place your thumb over the top of the test tube and shake to dissolve the salt. Record your observations. Using the dropper, add 5 drops of silver nitrate to the salt water. Record your observations.

4. Place a small piece of magnesium ribbon in a test tube. Add 5 drops of hydrochloric acid to the test tube. Touch the bottom of the test tube with your fingertips. Record your observations.

Observations

1. What did you observe as the candle burned? Smoke was given off; candle got smaller; wax melted and dripped.

What was left after the candle burned? Melted wax.

2. What did you observe as the paper burned? Answers will vary.

What was left after the paper burned? Black ash.

3. What did you observe when you added the salt to the water in the test tube and shook it? The salt "disappeared."

What did you observe when the silver nitrate was added to the salt water?
A white, cloudy substance formed.

4. What did you observe when the hydrochloric acid was added to the magnesium metal?
The acid started bubbling; magnesium disappeared; test tube was warm.

Analysis and Conclusions

1. Identify each of the following as either a physical change or chemical change. Give a reason for your answer.

a. Melting candle wax Physical. Wax just gets softer. _____

_____

b. Burning a candle Chemical. Candle changes to other substances. _____

_____

c. Tearing paper Physical. Paper is only made into smaller pieces. _____

_____

d. Burning paper Chemical. Paper changes to other substances. _____

_____

e. Dissolving table salt Physical. Salt is still present; can verify by tasting it in salt water or by _____

evaporating the water. _____

f. Mixing salt water and silver nitrate Chemical. A new substance is formed. _____

_____

g. Cutting a piece of magnesium ribbon Physical. Ribbon is only made into smaller pieces. ____

_____

h. Adding hydrochloric acid to magnesium metal Chemical. New substances are produced. _____

Energy change (heat) occurs. _____

2. Describe two observations you might make when a physical change occurs.

The original substances stay the same. No energy changes occur. _____

_____

_____

3. Describe two observations you might make when a chemical change occurs.

New substances are produced. Energy, usually in the form of heat, is given off or taken in. _____

_____

_____

Critical Thinking and Application

1. How could you show that dissolving the salt in water resulted in a physical change?

   The water could be evaporated, leaving the salt.

2. How could you show that adding acid to the magnesium ribbon resulted in a chemical

   change? After the reaction stops, you could evaporate the liquid. Magnesium will not be left, since it has

   changed as a result of the chemical reaction.

3. The following changes can sometimes indicate that a chemical change has occurred. Explain how each change might result from a physical, not a chemical, change.

   a. Change of color Object may be dyed.

   b. Loss of mass Evaporation may reduce the mass but is only a phase change.

   c. The substance seems to "disappear." Substance may dissolve but does not change to a new

   substance and may be reclaimed after the liquid is evaporated.

Going Further

Write out a recipe that involves cooking or baking. Identify each step in the recipe as resulting in either a physical change or a chemical change in the ingredients.

Laboratory Investigation

Chapter 4   Mixtures, Elements, and Compounds

8

Determining Solubility

You may want to refer students to pages 92–95 in their textbook for a general discussion of solutions.

Time required: 40 minutes

Background Information

Several factors affect the rate at which solids dissolve in liquids. These factors include the nature of the solute and solvent, the temperature, and the degree of fineness to which the solute has been ground. There is no general rule to predict how much solute will dissolve in a given solvent, but you can determine the effect certain variables have on the rate of solution.

In this investigation you will determine the amount of potassium nitrate that can be dissolved in 10 mL of water at a given temperature.

Problem

How can you determine the solubility of a substance in water?

You may want to discuss solubility with your students before performing this investigation. Assign each group of students two temperatures—one fairly high, the other low.

Materials *(per group)*

weighing paper
25 mL potassium nitrate
water
100-mL graduated cylinder
250-mL beaker
Celsius thermometer
Bunsen burner
2 test tubes
laboratory balance
1 test-tube holder
ice
glass stirring rod
safety goggles

Procedure

1. Place a small sheet of plain paper on the laboratory balance. Record the mass of the paper. Adjust the balance so that it registers 25 g more than the mass of the paper alone.

2. Slowly and carefully add potassium nitrate to the paper until the balance is again level. In this way, you have poured out 25 g of potassium nitrate.

3. Pour 10 mL of water into one test tube. Warm the test tube over the Bunsen burner until the first temperature assigned to you by your teacher is reached. Try to maintain this temperature throughout the next step.

4. Pour a small amount of potassium nitrate into the test tube. Stir carefully. If the potassium nitrate dissolves completely, add a little more. Continue until no more dissolves and a few small grains settle to the bottom of the test tube.

5. Record the exact temperature of the solution.

6. Find the mass of the paper and the remaining potassium nitrate again. Determine the amount of potassium nitrate you used by subtracting this amount from the original mass.

7. Repeat the procedure with another 10 mL of water. However, this time cool the water in ice until the second temperature assigned to you by your teacher is reached. Again determine the amount of potassium nitrate that dissolves in the water. Record the exact temperature.

8. Report your information to your teacher. He or she will compile all the information obtained by the class. In this way, you will find out how much potassium nitrate dissolves in 10 mL of water over a wide temperature range.

9. Graph your results and the results of your classmates in Graph 1.

Observations

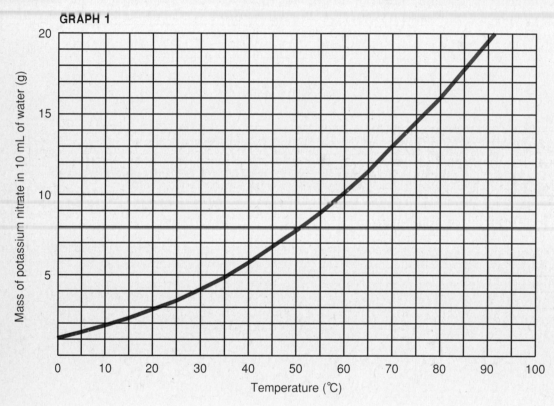

GRAPH 1

Analysis and Conclusions

1. What effect does temperature have on the amount of potassium nitrate that can be dissolved in a given amount of water? As the temperature increases, the amount of potassium nitrate that can be dissolved increases.

2. From the graph, predict how much potassium nitrate would dissolve in 10 mL of water at 60°C. 11 g

3. How much potassium nitrate do you think would dissolve in 100 mL of water at 60°C?

    110 g

4. To what temperature would 10 mL of water have to be heated to completely dissolve

    14 g of potassium nitrate? 72°C

Critical Thinking and Application

1. If the temperature of a saturated solution of potassium nitrate were to drop, what would

    you notice? The extra potassium nitrate would come out of solution and sink to the bottom of the test

    tube.

2. If 10 mL of a saturated solution of potassium nitrate were to cool from 60°C to 10°C, how much potassium nitrate would be found on the bottom of the test tube?

    8.5 g

3. Suppose you had measured the solubility of KNO_3 only at 10°C and 90°C. How might

    your solubility graph be inaccurate? By measuring only the extremes, you might draw the graph as

    a straight line. Solubilities in the range between these two temperatures would then appear higher than

    they actually are.

4. Based on the graph, how much KNO_3 do you think would dissolve in 10 mL of water at

    100°C? About 23–24 g

Going Further

Determine the solubility graph for sodium chloride (table salt). How does this graph differ from the graph for potassium nitrate?

© Prentice-Hall, Inc.

Laboratory Investigation

Relating Solubility and Temperature

You may want to refer students to pages 92–95 in the textbook for a general discussion of solubility.

Time required: 30 minutes

Background Information

The solubility of a substance indicates how much of that substance will dissolve in a given volume of water. The substance being dissolved is called the solute. The substance that does the dissolving is called the solvent. And the resulting substance is called the solution. So solubility tells you how much solute dissolves in a solvent. Solubility depends upon the nature of the solvent, the nature of the solute, and the temperature of the solution. In this investigation you will determine the effect of temperature on the solution process.

Problem

How does the temperature of a solution affect a solute's ability to dissolve?

Materials *(per group)*

ring stand and ring
wire gauze
400-mL beaker
Bunsen burner
4 medium-sized test tubes
    labeled A, B, C, D
triple-beam balance
30 grams of
    potassium nitrate (KNO_3)
100-mL graduated cylinder
stirring rod
test-tube rack
Celsius thermometer
tongs
graph paper
safety goggles
heat-resistant gloves

Procedure

1. Assemble a ring stand, wire gauze, Bunsen burner, and beaker as shown in Figure 1. Fill the beaker approximately half full of water and begin heating the water. Do not boil the water; just heat it to between 80° and 90°C. Use the thermometer to measure the water temperature, and turn off the burner once the water reaches the desired temperature range.

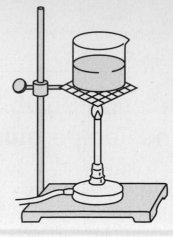

Figure 1

2. **CAUTION:** *In this part of the procedure, use extreme care in handling potassium nitrate. Do not allow it to come in contact with your skin.* Use the balance to measure a sample of potassium nitrate with a mass of 11 g. Place this sample in test tube A. Measure another sample with a mass of 8 g and place it in test tube B. Continue this procedure, measuring 6 g for test tube C and 4 g for test tube D.

3. Now add exactly 10 mL of water to each test tube.

4. Put the four labeled test tubes with their contents into the hot water in the beaker. Using a stirring rod, carefully stir the contents of each test tube to make sure all of the KNO_3 dissolves.

5. Allow the test tubes to remain in the hot water for 5 minutes. All of the KNO_3 in each test tube should now be completely dissolved. Remove the test tubes from the beaker with tongs and place them in the test-tube rack to cool. **CAUTION:** *Exercise care in handling the hot test tubes.*

6. Now place the thermometer in test tube A and note the temperature at which you first notice the clear liquid becoming cloudy as crystals form in the solution. Record this temperature in the appropriate column in the Data Table.

7. Quickly wipe the thermometer off, place it in test tube B, and note the temperature at which you first notice the liquid becoming cloudy as crystals form in the solution. Record this temperature in the Data Table.

8. Repeat this procedure for the two remaining test tubes. Record your data.

Observations

DATA TABLE

Test Tube	Temperature at Which Solute Starts to Form Crystals	Grams of KNO_3 per 10 mL Water	Calculated Grams of KNO_3 per 100 mL Water
A	~60°C	11	110
B	~48°C	8	80
C	~38°C	6	60
D	~27°C	4	40

Analysis and Conclusions

1. If 11 g of KNO_3 were dissolved in 10 mL of water in test tube A, how many grams of KNO_3 would have to be dissolved in 100 mL of water to give the same

   proportion? __110 g__ How many grams in test tube B? __80 g__ In test tube C? __60 g__ In

   test tube D? __40 g__ Record these answers in the appropriate column of the Data Table.

2. Prepare a graph of your data. Use the vertical axis for grams of KNO_3 per 100 mL of water and the horizontal axis for temperature. Your graph should have a total of four experimental points.   Students will probably need help with this part of the investigation. You may wish to review the steps in constructing a graph and choosing an appropriate scale. Using an overhead projector to construct the graph will facilitate students' understanding.

3. Connect your data points with a solid line. Then use a dotted line to extend the smooth line to 0°C. The line you have just drawn is called a solubility curve. It can be used to determine the solubility of KNO_3 at any given temperature. According to your curve,

   what is the solubility in g/100 mL of water of KNO_3 at 0°C? Approximately 15 g _____

4. What can you say about the shape of the solubility curve for KNO_3?

   It is a steep curve that goes steadily upward as temperature increases. _____

5. At 20°C, the accepted value for the solubility of KNO_3 is 30 g/100 mL of water. How does this compare with the value derived from your graph?

   Answers will vary. However, if students have done the investigation correctly and drawn the graph

   correctly, the two values should be close.

Critical Thinking and Application

1. This type of experiment can be used to determine the solubility of many different solutes. Name two ways in which the solubility curve for carbon dioxide gas in water would differ from the one you drew for KNO_3.

   The slope of the solubility curve would be downward, not upward, because much less solute would

   dissolve at any given temperature.

2. Solubility depends upon three factors: the nature of the solvent, the nature of the solute, and the temperature of the solution. Which factor was the variable in this investigation?

   Which factors were held constant? Temperature was the variable. The nature of the solvent and

   solute were constants.

3. Suppose you wanted to test the solubility of KNO_3 in various solvents. How might you go

   about doing this? The temperature of the solution and the volume of the solvents should be kept

   constant. You could keep adding KNO_3 to test tubes of 10 mL each of five different solvents at 25°C. You

   would then record the amount of solute that dissolved in each one.

4. A microbiologist wishes to prepare a solution of 650 g of KNO_3 in 1 L of water. Can she prepare this solution at room temperature? <u>No.</u>

Explain your answer. <u>Room temperature is about 25°C, and only 350 g of KNO_3 will dissolve in 1 L of water at this temperature. She would have to prepare the solution at a temperature of 40°C or higher.</u>

Going Further

Figure 2 shows the solubility curves for several different solutes. Using the graph, answer the following questions.

1. How many grams of KCl will dissolve in 100 mL of water at 80°C? <u>50.</u>

2. What two substances show a decrease in solubility as the temperature increases?

<u>$Ce_2(SO_4)_3$ $Yb_2(SO_4)_3$</u>

3. At what temperature are the solubilities of KCl and NaCl the same? <u>Approximately 30°C.</u>

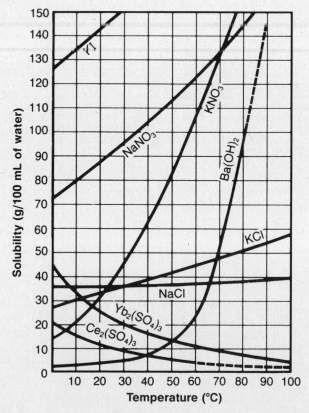

Figure 2

4. At a temperature of 80°C, 100 g of $Ba(OH)_2$ are completely dissolved in 100 mL of water. If the solution is cooled to about 62°C, how many grams come out of solution because they can no longer be dissolved? <u>70.</u>

5. At 10°C, what substance has the greatest solubility in 100 mL of water? <u>KI.</u>

Laboratory Investigation

Chapter 4   Mixtures, Elements, and Compounds

10

Elements, Mixtures, and Compounds

You may want to refer students to pages 88–104 in their textbook for a general discussion of the properties of mixtures, elements, and compounds.

Time required: 45 minutes

Background Information

When two elements are combined, a chemical reaction does not always occur between them. Instead, the two elements form a mixture in which the properties of the two elements are retained.

When a chemical reaction does take place, the two elements form a compound. The compound has physical and chemical properties that the individual elements alone do not have.

The two elements in a mixture can be separated on the basis of differences in their physical properties. The two elements in a compound, however, can only be separated as a result of another chemical reaction.

In this investigation you will observe how physical and chemical properties are affected when two elements are combined.

Problem

How do the properties of elements differ in mixtures and in compounds?

Materials (per group)

triple-beam balance	sulfur powder	250-mL beaker
forceps	iron powder	magnet
scoop	hand lens	safety goggles
Bunsen burner	test tube	
matches	test-tube clamp	

Procedure

Review procedure for "measuring out" a solid. Filter paper is best.

1. On your triple-beam balance, measure out 3 g of sulfur powder on a piece of paper.

2. Using the hand lens, observe the color of the sulfur and the size and shape of the particles. Record your observations in the Data Table.

3. Lift the edge of the paper containing the sulfur, place the magnet underneath, and move the magnet to see if it has any effect on the sulfur. Record your observations in the Data Table.

4. On your triple-beam balance, measure out 5 g of iron powder on a piece of paper.

5. Using the hand lens, observe the color of the iron powder and the size and shape of the particles. Record your observations in the Data Table.

6. Lift the edge of the paper containing the sulfur, place the magnet underneath, and move the magnet to see if it has any effect on the sulfur. Record your observations in the Data Table.

© Prentice-Hall, Inc.

7. Mix the iron and sulfur together on one piece of paper. Use the scoop to make sure the mixture is uniform throughout. Repeat step 2 for the mixture. Record your observations in the Data Table.

8. Repeat step 3 for the mixture. Record your observations in the Data Table.

9. Half-fill the beaker with cold water and set it aside. Carefully place the iron-sulfur mixture in a test tube. Light the Bunsen burner. Holding the test tube with the test-tube clamp, heat the iron-sulfur mixture for about 5 minutes. **CAUTION:** *Make sure that the mouth of the test tube is pointed away from you and others.* Move the test tube around in the flame so that all of the contents are evenly heated. Record your observations in the Data Table.   This step should be performed under a vent hood or in a well-ventilated area.

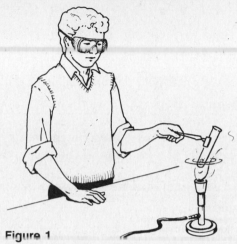

Figure 1

10. When you see no further changes occurring in the test tube, shut off the Bunsen burner and immediately put the test tube into the beaker of cold water. If the test tube does not break, wrap it in several layers of paper towel and hit it with a hammer to crack the glass.

11. Using the forceps, hand lens, and magnet, examine the substance formed in the test tube. Record your observations in the Data Table.   Caution students not to touch the substance or pieces of glass with bare fingers.

Observations

DATA TABLE

Physical Properties	Sulfur	Iron	Iron-Sulfur Before Heating	Iron-Sulfur After Heating
Color				
Shape of particle				
Size of particle				
Effect of magnet				

What did you observe when you began heating the test tube containing the mixture of sulfur and iron? The mixture liquefied and bubbled. A color change occurred. Smoke and fumes were given off.

Analysis and Conclusions

1. How did the properties of sulfur alone compare with the sulfur in the unheated iron-sulfur combination? <u>They were the same.</u>

   _____

2. How did the properties of iron alone compare with the iron in the unheated iron-sulfur combination? <u>They were the same.</u>

   _____

3. How did the properties of sulfur alone compare with the iron-sulfur combination after it was heated? <u>They were completely different. The iron-sulfur combination did not have any properties of</u> <u>sulfur.</u>

4. How did the properties of iron alone compare with the iron-sulfur combination after it was heated? <u>They were completely different. The iron-sulfur combination did not have any properties of</u> <u>iron.</u>

   _____

5. What kind of substance was the iron-sulfur combination before heating?
   <u>Mixture.</u>

6. What was the effect of heating the iron-sulfur combination?
   <u>A chemical change occurred.</u>

7. What kind of substance was the iron-sulfur combination after heating?
   <u>Compound.</u>

Critical Thinking and Application

1. Explain how you know that mixing the iron and sulfur together on the paper results in a mixture of the two substances. <u>The sulfur and iron each retain their physical properties.</u>

   _____

   _____

   _____

2. Explain how you know that heating the iron and sulfur together in the test tube results in a new compound composed of chemically combined iron and sulfur.

None of the original properties of iron and sulfur can be observed. A new substance is formed.

3. Why was it necessary to heat the test tube in order for a chemical reaction to occur?

This chemical reaction requires the addition of heat energy in order to occur.

4. The element sodium reacts explosively with water and the element chlorine is a yellowish-green poisonous gas. When chemically combined, sodium and chlorine form nonexplosive, nonpoisonous table salt. Explain how this can be.

When a chemical reaction occurs, the original properties of the reactants change and new properties result.

5. Identify each of the following as an element, a mixture, or a compound.

a. aluminum foil   Element.

b. air   Mixture.

c. water   Compound.

d. salt water   Mixture.

e. copper wire   Element.

f. steel   Mixture.

Going Further

The chemical combination of iron and sulfur produces the compound iron sulfide, also known as the mineral pyrite. Consult reference sources to find the properties and uses of pyrite.

Laboratory Investigation

11

Making Predictions Using Indirect Evidence

You may want to refer students to page 112 in their textbook for a general discussion of indirect scientific evidence.

Time required: 25 minutes

Background Information

How do scientists know what an atom looks like? After all, it is impossible to see an atom. Yet scientists have constructed models of an atom based on observations of how atoms behave. These observations are considered to be one type of indirect evidence for the structure of an atom.

Another type of indirect evidence comes from making predictions. Based on the model they have developed, scientists predict how atoms will behave in certain circumstances. They design experiments to test these predictions. If the predictions are shown to be accurate, they are taken as additional indirect evidence that the model is correct.

In this investigation you will use indirect evidence to determine the properties of an object you cannot see.

Problem

How can you determine the characteristics of something you cannot observe directly?

Materials *(per pair of students)*

shoe box, with cover, that contains small objects
laboratory balance

Pencils, piece of chalk, marbles, rubber stoppers, magnet, wooden spools, wood cube or wood beads are the kinds of items that may be placed in the boxes. Do this ahead of time.

Procedure

1. Obtain a sealed shoe box from your instructor.

2. Without opening the box, perform several tests such as tipping it, shaking it, sliding it, and finding its mass. In each case, record your observations in the Data Table. In each case, the observation could be of a sound or of the way the object behaved (rolling, sliding, and so on). You might also wish to find the mass of an identical box and lid that is empty. The difference in mass would be the mass of the object or objects inside.

3. On the basis of your observations, sketch the object or objects in Drawing 1. Include any other characteristics, such as mass.

© Prentice-Hall, Inc.

Observations

Describe some of the ways you tested the unknown objects to determine their characteristics. Record your descriptions in the Data Table.

DATA TABLE

Test	Observations

Analysis and Conclusions

DRAWING 1

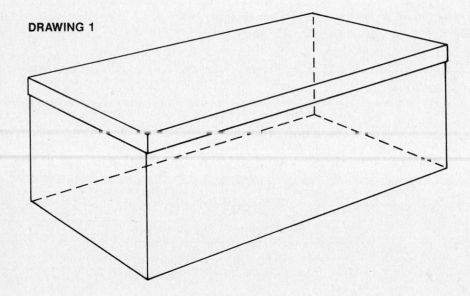

1. What senses did you use to determine a model of the object inside the box?

   Answers will vary but might include hearing and touch.

2. How does this kind of activity compare with the way scientists have learned about the atom? In both situations, indirect observations were made to determine characteristics.

Critical Thinking and Application

1. In what ways could you test your model of the contents of the box?

Put objects like those that you think are in the shoe box into an identical box and see if it behaves in the

same way. Determine the mass of the identical box and contents and see if it matches that of the shoe

box.

2. What kinds of special instruments could also be used to make indirect observations of the

contents of the box? X-ray machine, magnet, others.

3. If you used some of the special instruments you mentioned and the results did not agree
with your previous determination of the contents of the box, what would you need to

do? Redo the original experiment, making careful observations. From these observations, make new, but

logical, predictions.

4. Open the box and directly observe the object(s) inside. How does your observation

compare with your indirect determination? Answers will vary.

What does this tell you about the current model? The current atomic model represents scientists'

best attempts to predict atomic structure on the basis of careful experimentation and observation.

However, it is a model subject to change should new information be gathered and shown to be correct.

Going Further

1. Glue an object inside a shoe box. Trade boxes with another student who has done the same. Using knitting needles, determine the location and shape of the object by sticking the needles through the box.

2. How would you determine what kind of liquid was inside of a full, closed, opaque bottle? How would it be helpful if you had an identical empty bottle?

_____ *Laboratory Investigation* _____

Chapter 5   Atoms: Building Blocks of Matter   **12** ___

Investigating Rutherford's Model of the Atom

You may want to refer students to pages 116–117 in their textbook for a general discussion of Rutherford's experiment.

Time required:
Part A—20 minutes
Part B—30 minutes

Background Information

In 1911, Ernest Rutherford discovered that most of the atom is empty space. Almost all of the atom's mass is concentrated in an extremely small volume called the nucleus. The nucleus is located in the center of the atom. Rutherford discovered the existence of the nucleus in his famous scattering experiment. In this experiment, he aimed tiny, positively charged alpha particles at a very thin piece of gold foil. Rutherford observed that almost all the positively charged alpha particles passed through the gold foil with almost no deflection, or bending. This could only mean that the gold atoms in the sheet were mostly empty space!

However, Rutherford also observed that some particles were greatly deflected. In fact, a few bounced almost straight back from the gold foil. What could this mean? Rutherford knew that positive charges repel other positive charges. So he proposed that an atom had a small, positively charged center. He called this center the nucleus. In this investigation you will duplicate Rutherford's experiment.   This investigation would be accomplished most effectively as a teacher demonstration.

Problem

How can the presence of an "invisible" charged particle be detected?

Materials *(per group)*

sheet of white paper,
    50 cm × 20 cm
pencil
metric ruler
target platform with "nucleus"
    and ramp attached
tape
sheet of colored paper,
    30 cm × 20 cm
2 strips of posterboard,
    30 cm × 2 cm
strip of posterboard,
    20 cm × 2 cm
"alpha particle"   (magnet)
flour

For directions on how to build the target platform and ramp, see annotation following Going Further.

Procedure

Part A Constructing Your Setup

1. On the sheet of white paper, draw a series of lines lengthwise, 2 cm from each other. When you are finished there should be about ten parallel lines.

2. Tape this paper to the elevated ramp, as shown in Figure 1.

Figure 1

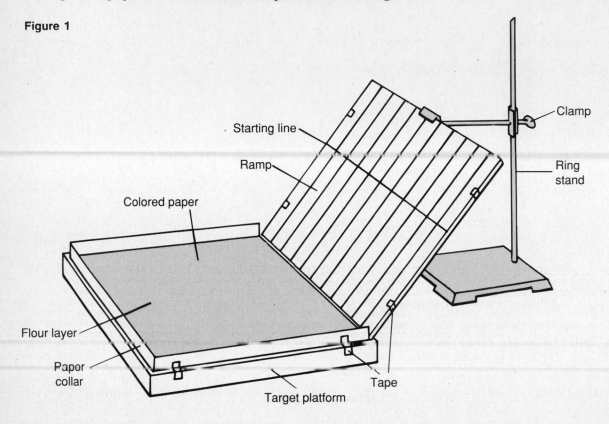

3. Tape the piece of colored paper to the target platform. **Note:** *Be sure that the edge of the paper does not interfere with the sliding of the "alpha particle" down the ramp to the platform.*

4. Place the alpha particle about halfway up the ramp. Make sure that the smooth surface of the alpha particle is facing down.

5. Allow the alpha particle to slide down the ramp and cross the platform. **Note:** *The alpha particle should not come to a stop until it is at least halfway across the target platform.* If it stops too soon, release it from a higher position on the ramp.

6. Adjust the height of the ramp until the alpha particle slides about 20 cm across the target platform before stopping. Using the ruler, draw a line across the ramp at this height.

7. Carefully sprinkle some flour on the platform so that the platform is entirely covered with flour. Use your ruler to create a smooth and even layer of flour. The flour will aid you in observing the path of the alpha particle.

Part B Duplicating Rutherford's Experiment

1. Release the alpha particle on the line on the ramp closest to you. Make sure that you position the alpha particle at your starting line.

2. Using the pencil, draw the exact path the alpha particle took in the flour on the colored paper. Label this line 1.

3. Smooth out the surface of the flour with your ruler.

4. Release the alpha particle along the next line. Draw its path on the colored paper. Label this line 2.

5. Repeat steps 2 and 3 until the alpha particle has been released from each of the vertical lines.

6. When you are finished, carefully remove the colored paper from the target platform. Carefully dispose of the flour.

Observations

1. On which areas of the target platform were the paths of the alpha particle straight

lines? Along the sides. _____

2. How many lines were deflected, or bent, on the target platform?

Answers will vary. _____

3. From your observations, locate the target "nucleus" on your colored paper. Draw its approximate size and shape. Attach the colored paper to this laboratory investigation.

Analysis and Conclusions

1. If the target platform represents an atom, is the target nucleus the same size as the atom?

Explain. No, the path of the alpha particle was not deflected every time it encountered the atom.

_____

2. Did the target nucleus attract or repel the alpha particle? Repel. _____

Explain. All of the paths of the alpha particle were deflected away from the nucleus.

_____

Critical Thinking and Application

1. In Rutherford's actual experiment, electric forces deflected the positive alpha particles from the positive target nuclei. In your duplication of Rutherford's experiment, what type of force did you use to deflect the alpha particle? How could you prove that you

used this type of force? The type of force that was used in the investigation was magnetic. To prove

this, students should suggest using a metal object, such as an iron nail or a paper clip, to show the

attraction of certain objects to the deflecting area.

_____

© Prentice-Hall, Inc.

2. In Rutherford's actual experiments, nearly all the alpha particles passed straight through and were not deflected at all. What does this tell you about the size of the nucleus of an atom? The nucleus must be very small.

As a result of these experiments, of what does an atom seem to mostly consist?
Mostly empty space.

3. In other experiments, Rutherford aimed beta particles, which are high-speed, negatively charged electrons, at the foil and screen. Predict the behavior of the beta particles. Most beta particles pass straight through. Some should be attracted to the nucleus of a nearby atom.

4. Rutherford repeated these experiments using foils made of metals other than gold. Predict the results of these experiments. The results were the same as they were for gold. All atoms have essentially the same structure.

Going Further

Find out about the contributions made by Crookes, Thomson, and Millikan to the discovery of the electron.

To construct the target platform and ramp, use corrugated cardboard about ⅛ of an inch thick. Cut two 20 cm × 30 cm pieces for the target platform and a 50 cm × 20 cm piece for the ramp. The target nucleus and alpha particle are 1-in-diameter ceramic disk magnets. Permanently glue one of the magnets to the underside of one of the platform boards about 10 cm from one end and in the middle. Cut four pieces of 1 in × 1 in wood to fit the platform. Nail, screw, or glue the two platform boards to the four pieces of wood, forming a flat cigar-shaped box. This will be the platform. Lay the ramp on top of the platform. Line up the sides of the ramp with the platform. Align one edge of the ramp 1 cm from the edge of the target platform that is closest to the ceramic disk. Tape the two parts together with 2-in ducting tape to form a hinge. Fold open the ramp and attach it to a ring stand. To make a collar around the platform, tape two 30 cm × 2 cm strips and one 20 cm × 2 cm strip of posterboard around the target platform. The collar will prevent the flour from getting all over the work area. The apparatus should now look like Figure 1. Label the other ceramic disk "alpha particle."

_____ *Laboratory Investigation* _____

13 ___

Relating Electrons and Probability

You may want to refer students to pages 124–126 in their textbook for a general discussion of the location of electrons in an atom.

Time required: 25 minutes

Background Information

Early theories of the structure of the atom described the movement of electrons around the nucleus as similar to the movement of the planets around the sun. Today scientists know this is not the case. Electrons do not travel around the nucleus in fixed orbits. Electrons move in an area known as the electron cloud. The electron cloud is a region in which electrons are likely to be found. Within the electron cloud, electrons are arranged in energy levels. Energy levels represent the most probable location in which an electron can be found. An energy level should not be confused with a specific path. For electrons do not have a path. In fact, scientists can speak only of the chances, or probability, of finding electrons at various locations—not of their exact position. In this investigation you will get a better understanding of probability and how it relates to electrons.

Problem

How can the movement of electrons outside the nucleus be described?

Materials *(per group)*

1 die
masking tape
1 sheet of graph paper having
   1½ squares to the centimeter

If you wish to prepare the dice prior to the investigation, tape all six sides and mark as follows: Place one dot on each of three sides, two dots on each of two sides, and three dots on the remaining side.

Procedure

1. Prepare your die in the following way: Tape all six sides. Mark three of the sides with one dot each, two of the sides with two dots each, and the remaining side with three dots.

2. Select a square near the center of the graph paper and color it red. This red square will represent the nucleus.

3. Roll the die and with each roll pencil in a square according to the following rules.
   ■ If a one is rolled, pencil in any square that is between 0 and 3 cm from the nucleus.
   ■ If a two is rolled, pencil in any square that is between 3 and 5 cm from the nucleus.
   ■ If a three is rolled, pencil in any square that is between 5 and 7 cm from the nucleus.

4. Repeat this procedure of rolling the die and marking the graph for 50 throws. Record your results in the Data Table.

© Prentice-Hall, Inc.

Observations

DATA TABLE

	Number of Squares Penciled In
0–3 cm (first energy level)	Approximately 25
3–5 cm (second energy level)	Approximately 16
5–7 cm (third energy level)	Approximately 9

1. The modern view of the movement of electrons in an atom is based on the concept of probability. What is the definition of probability? <u>Likelihood or chance of a particular form of</u> <u>some event occurring.</u>

_____

_____

2. In which range do you have the most darkened squares on your diagram?
<u>First range: 0–3 cm</u>

_____

3. Compare your diagram to that of a classmate. Are they identical?
<u>Diagrams will vary.</u>

_____

In what ways are they alike? Different? <u>Average concentration of penciled-in squares alike;</u> <u>distances from nucleus in each range different.</u>

_____

_____

Analysis and Conclusions

1. Based on your data, in what energy level is an electron most likely to be found?
<u>First energy level.</u> Least likely to be found? <u>Third energy level.</u>

2. If each square that you penciled in represents a chance of finding an electron in a particular location around the nucleus, where would you look first for an electron?

Explain your answer. _Close to the nucleus, within the 0–3 cm range. The penciled-in squares are_

closer together, representing the best chance of finding an electron.

_____

3. Can the exact position of an electron around the nucleus be determined?

No, the exact position of an electron cannot be determined.

What can be known about electrons? _The average energy of electrons and the areas of high_

probability of location can be known.

Critical Thinking and Application

1. Mathematically, the probability of an event occurring is equal to the number of favorable outcomes divided by the number of possible outcomes. According to the way you marked your die at the beginning of this investigation, what is the probability of an electron being found in the first energy level? The second? The third?

_1/2; 1/3; 1/6_

_____

2. Suppose you had rolled the die 100 times. How do you think your results would have compared with the results you obtained by rolling the die 50 times?

The probabilities should remain about the same, although the number of darkened squares in each area

would approximately double.

_____

_____

3. Suppose you wanted to determine the probability of a student being found at various locations in your school building at 10 AM. How might you investigate this problem?

Answers will vary. One method might be to take a sample of 30 students and record their whereabouts at

10 AM for several days. Another method might be to survey various areas of the building at 10 AM for

several days and record the number of students in each location.

_____

_____

© Prentice-Hall, Inc.

Going Further

Each energy level in an atom can hold only a certain number of electrons. The first energy level, closest to the nucleus, can hold at most 2 electrons. For the elements in the chart, the second and third energy levels are considered full when they have 8 electrons each. Using this information, fill in the chart below.

Element	Number of Electrons	Electron Arrangement			
		First Energy Level	Second Energy Level	Third Energy Level	Fourth Energy Level
Hydrogen	1	1			
Helium	2	2			
Carbon	6	2	4		
Oxygen	8	2	6		
Neon	10	2	8		
Sodium	11	2	8	1	
Aluminum	13	2	8	3	
Sulfur	16	2	8	6	
Chlorine	17	2	8	7	
Calcium	20	2	8	8	2

_____ *Laboratory Investigation* _____

14 __

The Alkaline Earth Elements

You may want to refer students to pages 150–151 in their textbook for a general discussion of the alkaline earth metals.

Time required: 45 minutes

Background Information

The arrangement of the elements in the periodic table is one of the most important achievements in modern chemistry. The physical and chemical properties of elements change in a regular pattern as you go both across the rows and down the columns of the periodic table. As a result, when elements close to each other in a row or column are compared, they have many of the same properties. However, when elements farther away from each other in a row or column are compared, they have more dissimilar properties.

The elements in Group 2 of the periodic table are known as the alkaline earth elements. Like all members of a group, or family, of elements, they have certain properties that change in a regular pattern within the group. One of these properties is the ability to form a precipitate, or solid substance, as a result of a chemical reaction. The precipitate cannot dissolve in water and eventually settles to the bottom of the container.

In this investigation you will compare the abilities of the alkaline earth elements to form precipitates as a result of a chemical reaction.

Materials *(per group)*

safety goggles
spot plate   Inexpensive polystyrene spot plates are available from laboratory supply companies.
sheet of notebook paper
dropper bottles of: If dropper bottles are not available, use 50-mL beakers containing the solutions
  magnesium nitrate   and dispense them using 10-cm lengths of glass tubing.
  calcium nitrate   To prepare solutions:
  strontium nitrate $Mg(NO_3)_2$ 0.2 M: dissolve 48.4 g in 1 L water
  barium nitrate $Ca(NO_3)_2$ 0.1 M: dissolve 24 g in 1 L water
  potassium carbonate $Sr(NO_3)_2$ 0.1 M: dissolve 21.2 g in 1 L water
  potassium sulfate $Ba(NO_3)_2$ 0.1 M: dissolve 26 g in 1 L water
  potassium chromate K_2CO_3 0.2 M: dissolve 28 g in 1 L water
                         K_2SO_4 0.2 M: dissolve 34.9 g in 1 L water
                         K_2CrO_4 0.2 M: dissolve 38 g in 1 L water

Procedure

1. Place the spot plate in the center of a sheet of notebook paper so that there are 4 spots running down and 3 spots running across. See Figure 1.

2. Along the side of the notebook paper next to each of the four spots, write the names of the four alkaline earth elements that are present in each nitrate compound listed in the materials you are using. Write them in the same order in which they are listed. See Figure 1.

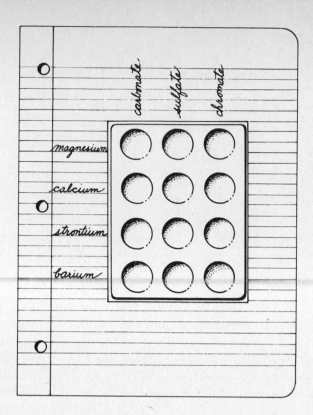

Figure 1

3. Along the top of the notebook paper next to each of the three spots, write the names of the three substances that are combined with potassium in the materials you are using. See Figure 1.

4. Put on your safety goggles. Place 3 drops of potassium carbonate in each of the four spots under the word Carbonate. Place 3 drops of potassium sulfate in each of the four spots under the word Sulfate. Place 3 drops of potassium chromate in each of the four spots under the word Chromate. Be very careful not to mix the liquid from one spot with the liquid from another.

5. Take the dropper bottle of magnesium nitrate and place 3 drops in each of the three spots in the row labeled Magnesium. Observe each spot carefully and record the result in the Data Table. Repeat this procedure using the dropper bottles containing calcium nitrate, strontium nitrate, and barium nitrate. Be very careful not to mix the liquid from one spot with the liquid from another.

6. After recording your results, wash your spot plate thoroughly with soapy water and a brush.

Observations

DATA TABLE

Alkaline Earth Metal	Carbonate	Sulfate	Chromate
Magnesium	white	clear	clear
Calcium	white	slight white color	clear
Strontium	white	white	clear
Barium	white	white	yellow

Analysis and Conclusions

1. Was there evidence of a chemical reaction occurring in any of the spots? Yes.

   Explain your answer. A color change occurred and a white or yellow precipitate resulted.

   _____

   _____

2. Which alkaline earth element formed the smallest number of precipitates? Magnesium.

3. Which alkaline earth element formed the greatest number of precipitates? Barium.

4. What is the relationship between the number of precipitates formed and the location of

   the alkaline earth element on the periodic table? The alkaline earth elements located further

   down in the column form more precipitates.

   _____

5. If the ability of an alkaline earth element to form a precipitate is an indication of its
   ability to chemically react with other substances, which is the most reactive element?

   Barium.

   The least reactive?

   Magnesium.

6. List the alkaline earth metals in order of their chemical reactivity, starting with the most

   reactive. Barium, strontium, calcium, magnesium.

   _____

7. How does the order of the elements you listed in question 6 compare to their order in

   the periodic table? It's the reverse of their order in the periodic table.

   _____

Critical Thinking and Application

1. Why were you cautioned not to mix the solution in one spot with the solution in another

   spot on your spot plate? Mixing would give incorrect results.

   _____

© Prentice-Hall, Inc.

2. Group 1 in the periodic table is known as the alkali metals. Based on your investigation of the Group 2 elements, predict the comparative reactivity of the elements in Group 1 of the periodic table.

Francium, cesium, rubidium, potassium, sodium, lithium.

3. If you had a solution containing a mixture of magnesium, strontium, and barium, how could you separate the three elements?
Hint: Review the information in the Data Table.

Add potassium chromate so that barium forms a precipitate. Pour off the liquid and add potassium

sulfate to it so that strontium forms a precipitate. Pour off the remaining liquid in which magnesium is

dissolved.

Going Further

Perform the procedure you described in your answer to question 3. Be sure to check the procedure with your teacher before starting. Describe your investigation in a laboratory report that includes title, problem, materials, procedure, observations, and conclusions.

_____ *Laboratory Investigation* _____

Chapter 6   Classification of Elements: The Periodic Table

15

Investigating the Activity Series of the Metals

You may want to refer students to pages 159–161 in their textbook for a general discussion of periodic properties.

Time required: 35 minutes

Background Information

One way to arrange the elements in the periodic table is by order of their activity. A metal is said to be more active than another metal if it will replace the less active metal from a solution of one of its compounds. This can be observed because the metal with the lower activity is "plated out" as pure metal on the piece of metal with the higher activity. By performing a series of experiments, you can develop a list of metals in order of their activity.

In this investigation you will test zinc, copper, and lead to see if they will replace each other in solutions of their compounds. Using your results, you can develop a short list in order of activity.

Problem

How can you determine the relative activities of zinc, copper, and lead?

Materials (*per pair of students*)

solutions	To prepare the solutions, add the following amounts to 1 L of water:		
copper sulfate	copper sulfate	$CuSO_4 \cdot 5H_2O$	62.5 g
lead acetate	lead acetate	$Pb(C_2H_3O_2)_2$	81.25 g
zinc sulfate	zinc sulfate	$ZnSO_4$	40.25 g

10-cm strips
  zinc
  lead
  copper
sandpaper
9 small test tubes
test-tube rack
safety goggles
masking tape

© Prentice-Hall, Inc.

Procedure

👁 **1.** Put on safety goggles.

2. Arrange the nine test tubes in three groups of three each. Using small pieces of masking tape, label the first three test tubes Lead Acetate, the next three Zinc Sulfate, and the last three Copper Sulfate. See Figure 1.

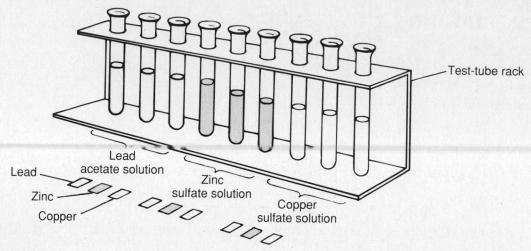

Figure 1

⚗ **3.** Fill the appropriately labeled three tubes one third full of lead acetate solution. Fill the appropriately labeled three tubes one third full of zinc sulfate solution. Fill the appropriately labeled remaining three tubes one third full of copper sulfate solution.

4. Clean the metal strips by rubbing with sandpaper. Using a separate tube for each strip of metal, place strips of lead, zinc, and copper in each of the three kinds of solutions.

▣ **5.** After several minutes, examine the strips for evidence of a reaction; remove them from the solutions if necessary. Record your observations in the Data Table. Also note if the solution changed color.

Observations

DATA TABLE

	Lead Acetate	Zinc Sulfate	Copper Sulfate
Lead	None	None	Copper deposited; solution becomes lighter blue
Zinc	Lead deposited	None	Copper deposited; solution becomes lighter blue
Copper	None	None	None

1. Which metal did not react with any of the solutions it was placed in?

Copper.

2. Which metal reacted with all but its own solution?

Zinc.

Analysis and Conclusions

1. List the metals in order of decreasing activity. Zinc, lead, and copper. _____

_____

2. How could you tell which of the three metals was the most active?

Zinc replaced both lead and copper in solutions of their compounds.

_____

Critical Thinking and Application

1. Magnesium is more active than zinc. How would a strip of magnesium have reacted in the

three solutions you studied? It would have reacted with all three solutions, replacing zinc, lead, and

copper.

2. Tin is less active than zinc but more active than lead. How would a strip of tin have

reacted in this investigation? It would have reacted with all but the zinc solution, replacing lead and

copper.

3. A strip of silver does not react with any of the solutions tested. What must be true about

silver? It is less active than copper, the least active metal studied so far. _____

_____

4. What experiment could you perform in order to determine if iron is more active than

copper? Place a strip of iron into copper sulfate. If the iron became coated with copper, then you would

know that iron is more active than copper.

_____

5. Metals like platinum and gold are often said to be inactive. What does this mean?

This means that platinum and gold do not tend to replace other metals in solutions of their

compounds.

Going Further

1. Read about plating with copper or silver. How is plating done commercially? How could
you do it in the laboratory?

2. Determine the activity of aluminum relative to the other metals.

© Prentice-Hall, Inc.

_____ *Laboratory Investigation* _____

16

The Law of Definite Composition

You may want to refer students to pages 174–178 in their textbook for a general discussion of bonding and the formation of compounds.

Time required: 45 minutes

Background Information

Many compounds are made of exactly the same elements but have very different physical and chemical properties. For example, carbon dioxide (CO_2), and carbon monoxide (CO), are both gases consisting of carbon and oxygen. Yet carbon dioxide is a harmless gas found in the body whereas carbon monoxide is a deadly gas when inhaled in sufficient amounts.

The reason for the difference between these two carbon–oxygen compounds is explained by the law of definite composition. This law states that the masses of the elements in a compound always occur in the same proportion. In other words, a carbon monoxide molecule consists of only 1 carbon atom and 1 oxygen atom. A carbon dioxide molecule consists of 1 carbon atom and 2 oxygen atoms. The difference in the number of oxygen atoms makes these two compounds very different from each other.

In this investigation you will compare the physical and chemical properties of water and hydrogen peroxide, both of which consist of hydrogen and oxygen.

Problem

How can two compounds consist of the same elements yet have different properties?

Materials *(per group)*

graduated cylinder
hydrogen peroxide, 3%   Available from pharmacy or supermarket
manganese dioxide
safety goggles
2 test tubes
test-tube rack
matches
2 wood splints

Procedure

1. Put on your safety goggles. Label one test tube H_2O (water) and the other H_2O_2 (hydrogen peroxide). Measure 5 mL of each compound and pour it into the appropriate test tube.

2. Observe the physical properties of each compound and record your observations in the Data Table on page 84.

© Prentice-Hall, Inc.

3. Put a small amount of manganese dioxide on the tip of one of the wood splints and add a little to each test tube. If you see evidence of a chemical reaction occurring, perform the following step: Light the unused wood splint with a match. Blow out the flame so that the wood is glowing at the edges. Insert the glowing splint into the test tube(s) in which a chemical reaction is occurring. Record your observations in the Data Table.

Better results will be obtained if one student keeps a thumb over the top of the test tube while another student lights the splint.

Observations

DATA TABLE

Compound	Physical Properties	Reaction With Manganese Dioxide
Water (H_2O)		
Hydrogen peroxide (H_2O_2)		

Analysis and Conclusions

1. How do the physical properties of water and hydrogen peroxide compare?

They are very similar. Both are clear, odorless liquids.

2. What effect did the manganese dioxide have on each compound?

It had no effect on water. Hydrogen peroxide bubbled rapidly when manganese dioxide was added.

3. How do the chemical properties of water and hydrogen peroxide compare?

Water does not react when manganese dioxide is added to it. Hydrogen peroxide reacts with manganese dioxide.

4. How do the formulas for the two compounds differ? Water is H_2O, and hydrogen peroxide is H_2O_2.

5. State a hypothesis to explain why water and hydrogen peroxide have different chemical properties. Hydrogen peroxide has one more oxygen atom than water in every molecule.

Critical Thinking and Application

1. The atomic mass number of hydrogen is 1.0. The atomic mass number of oxygen is 16.0.

   a. What is the proportion by mass of hydrogen to oxygen in water?

   2:16 or 1:8

   b. What is the proportion by mass of hydrogen to oxygen in hydrogen peroxide?

   2:32 or 1:16

2. Explain how the law of definite proportions explains the fact that although water and hydrogen peroxide consist of the same elements, they have different properties.

   The proportion by mass of hydrogen to oxygen is different for water and hydrogen peroxide, resulting in

   different properties.

3. Look up the atomic mass number of carbon in your periodic table. Mass number of

   carbon: 12.0

   a. What is the proportion by mass of carbon to oxygen in carbon monoxide?

   12:16 or 3:4

   b. What is the proportion by mass of carbon to oxygen in carbon dioxide?

   12:32 or 3:8

4. Explain how the law of definite proportions explains the fact that although carbon monoxide and carbon dioxide consist of the same elements, they have different properties.

   The proportion by mass of carbon to oxygen is different for carbon monoxide and carbon dioxide,

   resulting in different properties.

Going Further

The manganese dioxide used in this investigation is a catalyst. Using reference sources, find out what catalysts are and how they are used in chemical reactions. Describe an investigation you might perform to demonstrate the effect of a catalyst on a chemical reaction. Use a laboratory report format that includes title, problem, materials, procedure, observations, and conclusions.

Laboratory Investigation

Chapter 7   Atoms and Bonding

17

Comparing Covalent and Ionic Compounds

You may want to refer students to pages 178–188 in the textbook for a general discussion of ionic and covalent bonding.

Time required: 25 minutes

Background Information

Compounds are either covalent or ionic depending on the nature of the forces that hold them together. In ionic compounds, the force of attraction is between oppositely charged ions. This attraction is called an ionic bond. In covalent compounds, atoms are held together by an interaction between adjacent nuclei and shared electrons. These different forces account for many of the properties of ionic and covalent compounds, such as the degree of volatility (ability to turn into a gas) and solubility.

In this investigation you will examine the properties of a representative ionic compound, sodium chloride, and a representative covalent compound, paradichlorobenzene (PDB). The properties studied will be volatility, ease of melting, and solubility in water.

Problem

How do the properties of ionic and covalent compounds differ?

Materials *(per group)*

sodium chloride	Bunsen burner	ring stand with ring
paradichlorobenzene	wire gauze	safety goggles
evaporating dish	2 test tubes	

Procedure

1. Carefully smell each compound. If you can detect an odor, assume that the compound has a high volatility. Record your observations in the Data Table.

2. In turn, place small equal amounts of each substance in an evaporating dish. See Figure 1. Heat each sample with a burner flame and observe the time required to melt each sample. Make sure the room is well ventilated. As soon as the PDB melts, remove the flame. Record your results in the Data Table.

Figure 1

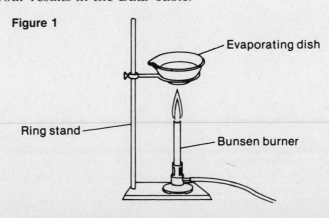

Evaporating dish

Ring stand

Bunsen burner

© Prentice-Hall, Inc.

3. Put a few small crystals of each substance in separate test tubes containing several milliliters of water at room temperature. Shake or stir and record in the Data Table how rapidly the substances dissolve in water.

Observations

DATA TABLE

Substance	Volatility	Melting Time	Solubility
Sodium chloride			
PDB			

1. Which compound was more volatile? PDB.

2. Which compound melted more quickly? PDB.

3. Which compound dissolved more easily in water?

Sodium chloride.

Analysis and Conclusions

1. Explain why the type of bond could determine the volatility of a substance.

Ionic bonds, such as those in sodium chloride, are stronger. Therefore, the material is held together more

tightly. More heat energy is required to separate the particles of the substance and allow them to escape

as gas.

2. Does the strength of the bond have anything to do with the time it takes to melt a substance? Explain. Yes. Ionic bonds are stronger. It takes more energy to melt ionic compounds.

3. Water molecules have parts that are negatively charged and parts that are positively charged. Which substances tend to dissolve easier in water, ionic or covalent? Why?

Ionic. Ionic compounds are made of charged particles, which interact with water molecules.

Critical Thinking and Application

1. What do your data tell you about the melting points of ionic and covalent compounds? How can you tell? You can tell that ionic compounds have higher melting points because it takes more time—and thus more heat energy—to melt them.

2. Which do you think would be more dangerous near an open flame: an ionic or a covalent compound? Why? A covalent compound would probably be more dangerous because it is more volatile.

3. Which type of compound—ionic or covalent—would you expect to have a higher boiling point? Why? Ionic, because a greater amount of energy is needed to separate the particles of the substance.

4. Suppose you had a sample of two compounds mixed together. Both compounds consist of fine white crystals. You know that one of the compounds is ionic and the other is covalent. How might you separate the two compounds?

Answers will vary. Probably the easiest method would be to mix the sample with water, separate out the undissolved covalent compound, then evaporate the water to retrieve the ionic compound.

Going Further

1. With adult supervision, test a variety of household materials to determine whether they are probably ionic or covalent. Vegetable oil, sugar, paraffin, and epsom salts are possible choices.

2. Certain substances when dissolved in water will conduct an electric current. Find out whether such substances are more likely to be ionic or covalent.

© Prentice-Hall, Inc.

Laboratory Investigation

18

Chemical Synthesis

You may want to refer students to page 209 in the textbook for a general discussion of synthesis reactions.

Time required: 45 minutes

Background Information

The word synthesis means to put together. In a chemical reaction involving synthesis, two or more substances combine to produce a single, more complex substance. The combined substances can be elements, compounds, or both. A written chemical equation involving synthesis should follow this general pattern:

Element or compound + Element or compound → Compound

For example, when a metal combines with oxygen from the air, the synthesis reaction that occurs is called oxidation. A compound called a metal oxide is produced. The reaction follows the general pattern:

Metal + Oxygen → Metal oxide

In this investigation you will synthesize copper oxide by heating copper metal in air.

Problem

How can a synthesis reaction be recognized?

Materials (per group)

ring stand and ring
wire gauze
Bunsen burner
triple-beam balance
evaporating dish
copper powder
scoop
safety goggles
tongs

© Prentice-Hall, Inc.

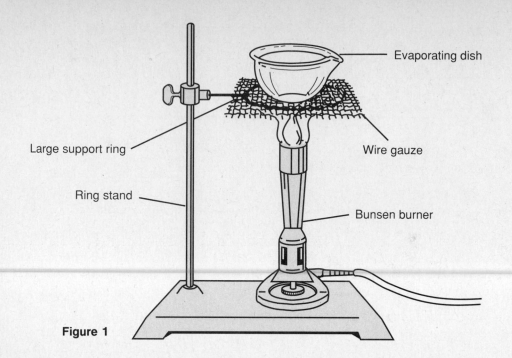

Evaporating dish

Large support ring

Ring stand

Wire gauze

Bunsen burner

Figure 1

Procedure

1. Set up the ring stand, ring, wire gauze, and Bunsen burner as shown in Figure 1.

2. Place the evaporating dish on the balance and find its mass to the nearest 0.1 g. Record the mass in Observations.

3. Add 5 g to the mass of the evaporating dish and move the riders on the balance to this number.

4. Using the scoop, slowly add copper powder to the evaporating dish until the pointer of the balance is on zero.

5. Place the evaporating dish containing the copper powder on the wire gauze. Make sure the copper powder is in a thin layer in the bottom of the dish.

6. Light the Bunsen burner and heat the evaporating dish for 5 to 10 minutes.

7. Turn off the Bunsen burner and allow the evaporating dish to cool for 5 to 10 minutes. Using the tongs, place the evaporating dish on the balance and find its mass. Record the mass in Observations.   Have students work on another short assignment during this ''wait time.''

Observations

1. Mass of empty evaporating dish Answers will vary.

2. Mass of evaporating dish + copper powder More than 5 g

3. Mass of copper powder 5 g

4. Mass of evaporating dish + copper oxide after heating Answers will vary, but should be more than answer to b.

5. Mass of copper oxide d − a

92

Analysis and Conclusions

1. What did you observe as a result of heating the copper powder that might indicate that a

   chemical reaction took place? The copper changed in color and texture.

2. What kind of chemical reaction occurred? Synthesis (oxidation).

3. What was the change in mass when the copper powder reacted with oxygen to form

   copper oxide? e − c

   Was this change an increase or decrease in mass? Increase.

4. Was this reaction endothermic or exothermic? Endothermic.

   Explain. Heat energy was needed in order for the reaction to occur.

5. Write a chemical equation for the synthesis reaction that took place.

   Copper + Oxygen → Copper oxide $2Cu + O_2 → 2CuO$

Critical Thinking and Application

1. Explain why there was a change in mass as a result of heating the copper powder in the

   evaporating dish. Oxygen from the air combined with the copper powder and added to the mass.

2. Find the percentage change in mass by using the following formula.

$$\text{Percentage change in mass} = \frac{\text{Change in mass}}{\text{Mass of copper}} \times 100 \text{ percent}$$

   Answers will vary.

3. There are actually two different oxides of copper produced as a result of this reaction.
   They are copper(I) oxide and copper(II) oxide. If copper is changed to copper(I) oxide,
   the percentage change in mass is 12 percent. If copper is changed to copper(II) oxide,
   the percentage change in mass is 25 percent. What must have been produced as a result
   of your investigation to give the percentage change in mass you calculated?

   Probably a mixture of copper(I) oxide and copper(II) oxide.

© Prentice-Hall, Inc.

4. Compare the percentage change in mass that you calculated with that calculated by your classmates. What variables would account for differences between your results and those of your classmates? Answers might include the heat of the burner flame; the length of time the copper was heated.

5. How could these variables be controlled so that the results obtained are more alike? Make sure that all burner flames are the same and the evaporating dishes are the same height above the burner. Heat for exactly the same amount of time.

6. Copper(II) oxide is black and copper(I) oxide is red. Using the scoop, examine the product of the reaction in the dish. Observe its color or colors. Does your observation support your answer to question 3? Explain. Probably yes. There will be both black and red particles in the evaporating dish.

Going Further

Use references to find out about other synthesis reactions. If time permits, do these reactions under your teacher's supervision.

Laboratory Investigation

Chemical Decomposition

You may want to refer students to pages 209–210 in the textbook for a general discussion of decomposition reactions.

Time required: 45 minutes

Background Information

Chemical decomposition is the opposite of chemical synthesis. In a decomposition reaction, a single compound is broken down into two or more simpler substances. These substances can be elements, other compounds, or both. A written chemical equation involving decomposition should follow this general pattern:

$$\text{Compound} \rightarrow \text{Element or compound} + \text{Element or compound}$$

For example, the compound potassium chlorate can be decomposed into potassium chloride and oxygen gas as a result of heating. Similarly, sodium chloride, or common table salt, can be decomposed into the elements sodium and chlorine by passing an electric current through it. This process is known as electrolysis.

In this investigation you will decompose water by electrolysis and determine the identity and relative amounts of the elements that are produced.

Problem

What are the products of the decomposition of water by electrolysis?

Materials *(per group)*

beaker, 600 mL or larger
bell wire   Commercial electrodes are inexpensive and available from laboratory suppliers.
dry cell, 6 volt
graduated cylinder
2 ring stands with test-tube
   clamps
matches
safety goggles
2 M sulfuric acid   To prepare, mix 112 mL 18 M H_2SO_4 in 888 mL distilled water.
wire strippers
2 wood splints

© Prentice-Hall, Inc.

Procedure

1. Put about 400 mL of water into the beaker. Fill each test tube with water. Holding your hand over the mouth of one test tube at a time to prevent spilling, turn each test tube upside down in the beaker. Clamp each test tube so that it is suspended just above the bottom of the beaker. See Figure 1.

2. Strip about 3 cm of insulation from one end of each piece of bell wire. Strip about 1 cm of insulation from the other end of each piece of bell wire. Attach the 1-cm bare end of one piece of wire to one of the terminals of the dry cell. **CAUTION:** *Do not attach the other wire to the other terminal yet.*

3. Bend the wires so that they trail over the edge of the beaker. Each 3-cm bare wire end should be placed in one of the test tubes. See Figure 1. Have your teacher check your setup to be sure it is correct before proceeding. After doing the next step, you will not be able to put your hand in the water.   Check student setups before allowing them to proceed with step 4.

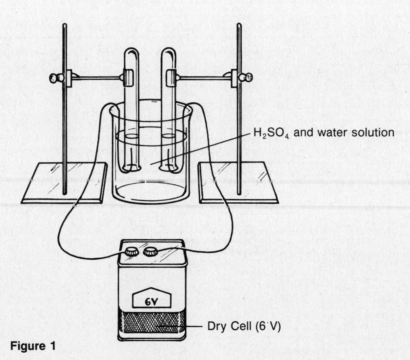

H₂SO₄ and water solution

Dry Cell (6 V)

Figure 1

4. Attach the remaining loose end of wire to the other terminal of the dry cell. Put on safety goggles. Without splashing, carefully add 50 mL of 2-M sulfuric acid to the water in the beaker. Record your observations. **CAUTION:** *Do not put your hands in the beaker for any reason.*

5. Allow the reaction to proceed for about 10 minutes or until no water is left in one of the test tubes. Disconnect the wires from the dry cell.

6. Remove the test tube with the least amount of water in it from the clamp. Hold it with a paper towel and keep your thumb over the top. Have a member of your lab group light one of the splints so that it is flaming and put it in the test tube. Record your observations. **CAUTION:** *Be careful when working with a burning splint.*

7. Remove the remaining test tube from the clamp and follow the same procedure as in step 6, but this time blow out the flame before placing the splint in the test tube. Record your observations.

8. Dispose of your acid solution as instructed by your teacher.

Observations

1. What did you observe happening in the test tubes when you added the acid?

   Bubbling began to occur and the water level began to fall.

   _____

2. What did you observe when you put the flaming splint in the first test tube?

   It made a loud "pop" and the flame went out.

3. What did you observe when you put the glowing splint in the second test tube?

   The glowing splint burst into flame. Or it may just have glowed more brightly.

4. To which battery terminal (positive or negative) was the test tube with the greater

   amount of water connected? Positive.

5. To which battery terminal (positive or negative) was the test tube with the lesser amount

   of water connected? Negative.

Analysis and Conclusions

1. What happened when acid was added to each test tube?

   A chemical reaction occurred. Bubbles were produced and the water level fell.

   _____

2. What caused the water level in the test tubes to change?

   As a result of the reaction, gas was produced and this displaced the water.

   _____

3. What gas was produced in the test tube that had the lesser amount of water?

   Hydrogen.

4. What gas was produced in the test tube that had the greater amount of water?

   Oxygen.

5. Is this reaction endothermic or exothermic? Endothermic.

   Explain. An electric current provided the energy.

   _____

© Prentice-Hall, Inc.

6. Write a chemical equation for the decomposition reaction that took place.

Water → Hydrogen + Oxygen 2H$_2$O → 2H$_2$ + O$_2$

Critical Thinking and Application

1. Identify the gas that was produced at the positive terminal.

Oxygen.

2. Identify the gas that was produced at the negative terminal.

Hydrogen.

3. Would you observe different results if you repeated the investigation but reversed the terminals to which the wires were attached? Yes.

Explain. Hydrogen will always be formed at the negative terminal and oxygen at the positive terminal.

4. Why were different amounts of the two gases produced? *Hint:* Look at the chemical formula for water. Water consists of two parts hydrogen combined with one part oxygen. Therefore, twice as much hydrogen as oxygen will be produced.

5. Did the sulfuric acid undergo a chemical change? No.

Why was the sulfuric acid necessary? The electric current is conducted better than with water alone.

Going Further

The nitrogen cycle and the carbon–oxygen cycle occur in nature and consist of many synthesis and decomposition reactions involving these elements. Use references to find out about the steps in these cycles. Identify each step as either a synthesis or decomposition reaction.

Laboratory Investigation

20

Single-Replacement Reactions

You may want to refer students to page 210 in the textbook for a general discussion of single-replacement reactions.

Time required: 30 minutes

Background Information

In nature, elements can occur either free, meaning uncombined with other elements, or chemically combined in a compound. The tendency of a particular element to combine with other substances is a measure of the activity of that element. The more active an element is, the more likely it is to combine. In a single-replacement reaction, an uncombined element replaces a less active element that is combined in a chemical compound. The less active element is then freed from the compound.

For example, in the reaction

Zinc + Copper sulfate → Zinc sulfate + Copper

zinc replaces the less active copper, combines with sulfate, and frees the copper from the compound.

In this investigation you will observe how various metals undergo single-replacement reactions when placed in acid. If the metal is more active than the hydrogen in the acid, it will replace the hydrogen and hydrogen gas will be released.

Problem

How does a single replacement reaction occur?

Materials *(per group)*

safety goggles
5 test tubes
test-tube rack
1 M hydrochloric acid   Add 86 mL 6 M HCl to form 1L of solution.
graduated cylinder
zinc   Mossy zinc.
copper   Cut up uninsulated wire or pieces of copper sheeting into 1-cm lengths.
aluminum   Aluminum shot or turnings.
iron   Small nails or pellets.
magnesium   Ribbon, cut in 1-cm lengths.

© Prentice-Hall, Inc.

Procedure

1. Label each test tube with the name of one of the metals listed in the materials.

2. Put on your safety goggles. Carefully pour 5 mL of hydrochloric acid into each test tube.

3. One at a time, place the appropriate metal in each test tube. Observe what happens to the metal in each test tube and feel each test tube as the reaction proceeds. Record your data in Observations.
   If reactions do not occur as indicated, rub the metal with sandpaper to remove possible oxidized coating.

4. When you have completed the investigation, carefully pour off the acid, rinse the metal several times with water, and put it into a container provided by your teacher. Do not put any unused metal in the sink.

Observations

1. Magnesium   Rapid bubbling; magnesium disappears.

2. Aluminum   Rapid but less active bubbling compared to magnesium.

3. Iron   Bubbles produced very slowly.

4. Copper   No reaction.

5. Zinc   Bubbles produced slowly.

Analysis and Conclusions

1. Write the single-replacement reaction that occurred between the acid and each metal.

   a. Magnesium   Magnesium + Hydrochloric acid → Magnesium chloride + Hydrogen gas

   $Mg + 2HCl \rightarrow MgCl_2 + H_2$

   b. Aluminum   Aluminum + Hydrochloric acid → Aluminum chloride + Hydrogen gas

   $2Al + 6HCl \rightarrow 2AlCl_3 + 3H_2$

   c. Iron   Iron + Hydrochloric acid → Iron(III) chloride + Hydrogen gas

   $2Fe + 6HCl \rightarrow 2FeCl_3 + 3H_2$

d. Copper No reaction.

_____

e. Zinc Zinc + Hydrochloric acid → Zinc chloride + Hydrogen gas

$Zn + 2HCl → ZnCl_2 + H_2$

2. Were these reactions endothermic or exothermic? Exothermic.

Explain. The test tubes in which the reactions occurred felt warm to the touch.

_____

Critical Thinking and Application

1. Which of the metals are more active than hydrogen? Magnesium, aluminum, iron, zinc.

_____

2. Which of the metals are less active than hydrogen? Copper.

_____

3. What could you do to prove that hydrogen gas was produced as a result of these

reactions? Insert a flaming splint into a test tube in which a reaction occurred. A "pop" is heard as the

hydrogen burns.

_____

4. The rate at which hydrogen gas is produced as a result of these single-replacement
reactions is an indication of the relative activity of the metals. List the metals in order of

their activity from most active to least active Magnesium, aluminum, zinc, iron.

_____

5. Nonmetals can also be involved in single-replacement reactions. If chlorine is more active
than bromine, write the equation for the reaction between chlorine and potassium

bromide. Chlorine + Potassium bromide → Potassium chloride + Bromine

$Cl_2 + 2KBr → 2KCl + Br_2$

© Prentice-Hall, Inc.

Going Further

Identify each of the following chemical equations as representing a synthesis, decomposition, or single-replacement reaction. Write a balanced equation for each reaction.

1. Silver nitrate + Copper → Copper nitrate + Silver

$2AgNO_3 + Cu \rightarrow Cu(NO_3)_2 + 2Ag$ SR

2. Hydrogen + Oxygen → Water

$2H_2 + O_2 \rightarrow 2H_2O$ S

3. Aluminum + Zinc chloride → Aluminum chloride + Zinc

$2Al + 3ZnCl_2 \rightarrow 2AlCl_2 + 3Zn$ SR

4. Aluminum hydroxide → Aluminum oxide + Water

$2Al(OH)_3 \rightarrow Al_2O_3 + 3H_2O$ D

5. Barium chloride → Barium + Chlorine gas

$BaCl_2 \rightarrow Ba + Cl_2$ D

Laboratory Investigation

Chapter 8   Chemical Reactions

21

Double-Replacement Reactions

You may want to refer students to page 211 in the textbook for a general discussion of double-replacement reactions.

Time required: 30 minutes

Background Information

Some of the most impressive chemical reactions are double-replacement reactions, also called ion-exchange reactions. In a double-replacement reaction, a clear solution of an ionic compound is added to a clear solution of another ionic compound. The positive ions of one compound react with the negative ions of the other compound to form a precipitate, a gas, or water. When a precipitate forms, the result can be very dramatic. The precipitate is an insoluble solid substance that may produce a sudden bright color in the remaining clear solution.

In this investigation you will perform a double-replacement reaction and observe and interpret the results.

Problem

How does a double-replacement reaction occur?

Materials (*per group*)

safety goggles
triple-beam balance
2 250-mL beakers
weighing paper
lead nitrate
potassium iodide
stirring rod
graduated cylinder

Procedure

1. Put on safety goggles. Place a piece of weighing paper on the balance and note its mass. Add 3 g to the mass of the paper and move the riders to this number. Measure out 3 g of lead nitrate and place it in one of the beakers. Discard the paper.

2. Add 50 mL of distilled water to the beaker and stir thoroughly to make sure that all the solid has dissolved. Rinse off the stirring rod and wipe it dry. Label the beaker Lead nitrate solution.

3. Repeat steps 1 and 2 using potassium iodide. Label the beaker Potassium iodide solution.

4. Pour the solution from one beaker into the other beaker and observe the results. Stir with the stirring rod and observe.

5. To dispose of your product, put it in the waste container indicated by your teacher. Do not spill the product down the sink. Rinse the beaker once with tap water and dispose of this material in the waste container. Thoroughly wash the beakers and stirring rod with soap and water.

Observations

1. What did you observe when you mixed the lead nitrate with water?

A clear solution was formed.

2. What did you observe when you mixed the potassium iodide with water?

A clear solution was formed.

3. What did you observe when you mixed the two solutions together?

A solid yellow substance (precipitate) was formed.

4. Did stirring the combination of the two solutions result in any change? No.

Explain. The yellow precipitate is insoluble in water.

Analysis and Conclusions

1. What ions were present in the lead nitrate solution? Lead ions and nitrate ions.

2. What ions were present in the potassium iodide solution? Potassium ions and iodine ions.

3. Write an equation for the reaction that took place. Lead nitrate + Potassium iodide → Lead

iodide (s) + Potassium nitrate $Pb(NO_3)_2 + 2KI \rightarrow PbI_2 (s) + 2KNO_3$

Critical Thinking and Application

1. A double-replacement reaction is also called an ion-exchange reaction. Describe the exchange of ions that occurred in this investigation. The positive lead ion from the lead nitrate combined with the negative iodine ion from the potassium iodide. The positive potassium ion from the potassium iodide and the negative nitrate ion from the lead nitrate remained in solution.

2. What must always be one of the products of a double-replacement reaction?
   A solid, a gas, or water.

3. What must the other product(s) always be? A soluble substance.

4. Describe what would happen if the product you obtained in this reaction were filtered through a filtering apparatus. The yellow solid would remain in the filter and a clear liquid would filter through.

Going Further

Identify each of the following chemical equations as representing a synthesis, decomposition, single-replacement, or double-replacement reaction. Write a balanced equation for each reaction.

1. Carbon monoxide → Carbon + Oxygen

   $2CO \rightarrow 2C + O_2$ D

2. Sodium + Water → Sodium hydroxide + Hydrogen gas

   $2Na + 2H_2O \rightarrow 2NaOH + H_2$ SR

3. Aluminum sulfate + Barium chloride → Aluminum chloride + Barium sulfate

   $Al_2(SO_4)_3 + 3BaCl_2 \rightarrow 2AlCl_3 + 3BaSO_4$ DR

4. Aluminum + Chlorine → Aluminum chloride

   $2Al + 3Cl_2 \rightarrow 2AlCl_3$ S

5. Sodium carbonate + Calcium hydroxide → Sodium hydroxide + Calcium carbonate

   $Na_2CO_3 + Ca(OH)_2 \rightarrow 2NaOH + CaCO_3$ DR

© Prentice-Hall, Inc.

_____ *Laboratory Investigation* _____

Comparing Reaction Rate and Catalysts

You may want to refer students to pages 215–218 in the textbook for a general discussion of reaction rates and catalysts.

Time required: 25 minutes

Background Information

Catalysts are substances that speed up chemical reactions even though they themselves are not used up. A small amount of a catalyst may have a great effect upon a reaction. Catalysts are often used in industry to speed up production. In this investigation you will study a chemical reaction and determine which materials act as a catalyst to speed up the reaction.

Problem

How do catalysts speed up a chemical reaction?

Materials *(per group)*

7 test tubes
35 mL 3% hydrogen
   peroxide solution
small quantities:
   manganese dioxide
   chromium oxide
   calcium oxide
   aluminum oxide
   cobalt oxide
   silicon dioxide

Procedure

1. Pour about 5 mL of hydrogen peroxide into each of seven test tubes. Note if any gas is produced. Look for bubbles.

2. Add one of the other substances to each of six test tubes, using the seventh as a control. Note if any gas is produced. (The gas is oxygen.)   Students can test for oxygen by inserting a glowing splint into the test tubes.

3. Record your observations in the Data Table.

Observations

DATA TABLE

Substance Added	Effect (Gas Produced?)
Manganese dioxide	Yes
Chromium oxide	Yes
Calcium oxide	No
Aluminum oxide	No
Cobalt oxide	Yes
Silicon dioxide	No
(Control)	No

1. Which substances produced a gas (oxygen)? <u>Manganese dioxide, chromium oxide, cobalt oxide.</u>

_____

_____

2. Was there a difference in the rate at which the gas was produced? <u>Yes.</u>

   Explain. <u>Manganese dioxide produced gas much faster than the other substances did.</u>

_____

_____

Analysis and Conclusions

1. Which substances acted as catalysts? <u>Manganese dioxide, chromium oxide, cobalt oxide.</u>

_____

2. Are some of the substances more effective catalysts than others?

   <u>Yes, manganese dioxide speeds up the reaction greatly.</u>

_____

3. How much manganese dioxide would be needed to catalyze a great amount of hydrogen

   peroxide? Explain. <u>Very little. It does not get changed in the reaction.</u>

_____

Critical Thinking and Application

1. What is the purpose of the control in this investigation?

   To give a basis for comparison in order to determine if a reaction has occurred in the other tubes.

2. Based on this investigation, do you think that often more than one substance can act as a

   catalyst in the reaction? Why? Yes, because in this investigation, three different substances sped up

   the release of oxygen gas.

3. Do you think that some substances might be better catalysts than others? Explain.

   Yes, because some substances will cause the reaction to progress faster than others. In this case,

   manganese dioxide was the best catalyst.

4. Can you think of circumstances in which the addition of a catalyst might not be a good

   idea? Any situation in which a faster reaction might be harmful. For example, some reactions will

   produce an explosion or overheating if they are allowed to proceed too rapidly.

Going Further

1. Enzymes are catalysts produced in the body that help the body digest certain foods. Make a list of several important enzymes and their function.

2. Newer cars are designed with catalytic converters that take the exhaust and change it into harmless products before releasing the exhaust into the environment. Find out what substances are changed and what they become.

© Prentice-Hall, Inc.

Laboratory Investigation

Testing Unknown Substances Using Acid–Base Indicators

You may want to refer students to pages 226–229 in the textbook for a general discussion of acids and bases.

Time required: 40 minutes

Background Information

Indicators are special chemicals that can show whether a given substance is an acid, a base, or neither. Indicators usually react with an acid or a base to form a slightly different chemical with a different color. Some examples of indicators are litmus paper and phenolphthalein. In this investigation you will test two unknown substances to see whether they are acidic or basic.

Problem

How can you determine whether a substance is an acid or a base? What happens when an acidic solution and a basic solution are mixed together?

Materials (per group)

solution A   0.01 M; 4.0 g of NaOH/L of solution
solution B   0.01 M; 8.3 mL of concentrated HCl/L of solution
10-mL graduated cylinder
4 test tubes
stirring rod
red litmus paper
blue litmus paper
1 mL 1% phenolphthalein
   solution
wire gauze
ring stand and ring
Bunsen burner
magnifying lens
small pieces of zinc, 1 g
2 medicine droppers
safety goggles
heat-resistant gloves

Procedure

👁 **1. CAUTION:** *Put on safety goggles.*

👁 **2.** Obtain 5 mL of solution A in a test tube and 5 mL of solution B in another test tube.
   CAUTION: *Use care when measuring and pouring solutions A and B. Wash any spills immediately with cold water.* Label the test tubes appropriately A and B.

3. Using a medicine dropper, place a drop from test tube A on a piece of blue litmus paper. Record any color change of the litmus paper in the Data Table.

© Prentice-Hall, Inc.

4. Using the same medicine dropper, place another drop from test tube A on red litmus paper. Record any color change in the Data Table.

5. Repeat steps 3 and 4 using solution B and a clean medicine dropper.

6. Put two drops of phenolphthalein solution into each test tube. Note the results in the Data Table.

7. Pour the contents of tubes A and B into a 200-mL beaker. Note the result of mixing the two solutions. Then place the beaker and its contents on a wire gauze on a ring stand as shown in Figure 1. Position a Bunsen burner beneath the beaker and light it. **CAUTION:** *Be careful when lighting and using the Bunsen burner.* Heat the beaker for 10 minutes or until the liquid has boiled away, leaving a dry residue.

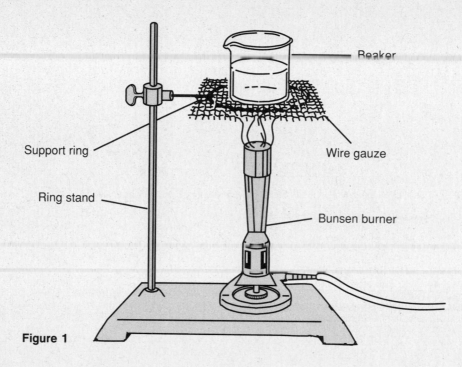

Figure 1

8. Allow the beaker to cool. Then examine the remaining residue with a magnifying lens.

9. Obtain 5 mL of the two solutions again in separate labeled test tubes. Put a few small pieces of zinc into each test tube and note the results in the Data Table.

Observations

DATA TABLE

Solution	Response to Litmus		Response to Phenolphthalein	Reaction With Zinc
	Red	**Blue**		
Solution A	Blue	No change	Magenta	No gas formed
Solution B	No change	Red	Clear	Produces gas bubbles

1. Which solution turned litmus paper red? B. _____

2. Which solution turned litmus paper blue? A. _____

3. Which solution produced a color change in phenolphthalein? A. _____

4. Which solution reacted with zinc to produce gas bubbles? B. _____

Analysis and Conclusions

1. Litmus paper turns blue in the presence of a base and red in the presence of an acid.

   Which solution, A or B, is an acid? __B.__ On a pH scale of 1 to 14, what would be the

   approximate pH of the solution you selected? Below 7. _____

2. Phenolphthalein indicator turns bright magenta (purplish red) in solutions that have a pH greater than 8. Solution B was hydrochloric acid (HCl). Solution A was sodium hydroxide (NaOH). What do you think was the pH of the solution that resulted when you mixed equal amounts of solution A and solution B?

   The resulting solution's pH is below 8, about 7. _____

   What was the identity of the white residue remaining after the boiling?

   The residue is impure sodium chloride, NaCl. _____

3. What do you think was the identity of the gas given off when zinc reacted in one of the

   solutions? Hydrogen gas. You may perform a test on this gas and collect some of the gas in a test tube

   by inverting it over the first tube. This can be ignited with a match to get a small "pop." _____

4. Write the balanced equation for mixing solutions A and B together.

   $HCl + NaOH \rightarrow H_2O + NaCl$ _____

5. Write the balanced equation for the reaction that occurred between zinc and

   solution B. $2HCl + Zn \rightarrow ZnCl_2 + H_2$ _____

Critical Thinking and Application

1. Based on the equation you wrote for mixing solutions A and B together, what is the general reaction for the combination of an acid and a base?

   Acid + Base $\rightarrow$ Salt + Water _____

© Prentice-Hall, Inc.

2. Based on the equation you wrote for the reaction between zinc and solution B, what happens when an acid comes in contact with a metal?

Hydrogen gas is produced.

3. Suppose you had mixed unequal amounts of solution A and solution B. What do you think the pH of the resulting solution would be?

It would be less than 7 if you mixed more acid than base, and greater than 7 if you mixed more base than acid.

4. Design an experiment in which you could investigate the effect of mixing unequal amounts of acid and base.

Answers will vary. Students should, however, keep the acid–base or base–acid ratio the same when testing unequal amounts. If they test two parts acid to one part base, then they should test two parts base to one part acid.

Going Further

The indicator litmus is a commonly used lab compound. Find out where it was first obtained.   It is a large molecule (molecular weight 3300) that can be isolated from certain lichens.

Laboratory Investigation

Chapter 9   Families of Chemical Compounds

24

Testing Commercial Antacids

You may want to refer students to pages 230–232 in the textbook for a general discussion of acids, bases, and neutralization.

Time required: 40 minutes

Background Information

Common indigestion is often caused by excess stomach acid. Popular stomach remedies, or antacids, claim to remove the symptoms of acid indigestion by neutralizing excess stomach acid.

In this investigation you will test the effectiveness of several commercial antacids by determining whether the antacid will neutralize a given volume of hydrochloric acid.

Problem

Do commercial stomach remedies neutralize acid?

Materials *(per group)*

100-mL beaker
medicine dropper
HCl, 1 M
methyl orange indicator
several different commercial
    antacids
mortar and pestle
stirring rod
distilled water

The antacids should be noneffervescent. For best results use milk of magnesia liquid and two different brands of tablets.

Procedure

1. Pour 10 mL of HCl into a beaker.

2. Put two to three drops of methyl orange indicator into the beaker and record the color in the Data Table.

3. Fill a clean dropper with the liquid antacid and add the liquid drop by drop to the beaker, stirring after each drop. In the Data Table, record the number of drops you add and any color changes you see.

4. Continue to add drops and stir until there is no more color change.

5. Use the mortar and pestle to grind one of the antacid tablets into a fine powder. While grinding, slowly add 10 mL of distilled water.

6. Fill a clean dropper with the powder-water mixture. Fill a clean beaker with 10 mL of HCl. Repeat steps 2, 3, and 4 for this mixture. (If you run out of tablet mixture, you may have to grind another tablet.)

7. Repeat steps 5 and 6 for the second brand of antacid tablet.

Observations

DATA TABLE

Color of Indicator in Acid	Substance Added to Acid	Number of Drops	Change in Color	Other Observations
Red	Liquid antacid			
Red	Tablet #1			
Red	Tablet #2			

Answers will vary, but there should be a change first to orange as the acid is neutralized, then to yellow as the solution becomes basic.

Analysis and Conclusions

1. Can you conclude that commercial antacids do neutralize stomach acid? _Yes._

   On what do you base this conclusion? _The methyl orange indicator changed from red (acid) to_ _orange (neutral)._

2. What must be the nature of the substances that make up antacids? How can you tell?
   They must be basic, because they neutralize acid and, when in excess, turn methyl orange yellow.

Critical Thinking and Application

1. Is it possible to determine from this investigation whether one type of antacid is more effective, or better, than another? Explain. _No, unless perhaps one considers the amount of each_ _substance that is required. All substances were able to neutralize acid._

2. When testing some of the antacids, you may have observed a gas being released. What was this gas? _CO_2_

3. What is the general chemical reaction for the process that produced the gas you named in question 2? _A carbonate plus acid yields salt, water, and carbon dioxide._

Going Further

Collect advertisements for various types of antacids from magazines and newspapers. Have a class discussion or debate about whether the claims of such ads are "scientific."

Laboratory Investigation

25

Acids and Bases From Home

You may want to refer students to pages 230–232 in the textbook for a general discussion of acids, bases, and neutralization.

Time required: Part A—20 minutes
Part B—25 minutes

Background Information

The science laboratory is not the only place where acids and bases are found. Many items commonly found at home are acids or bases. For example, many of the foods you eat contain acids. Commonly used cleaning products owe their effectiveness to the fact that they are alkaline, or contain bases.

In this investigation the strength of common acidic and basic substances found in the home will be determined using a method known as titration. To titrate an acidic substance, a basic solution whose concentration is known is added to the acid until the acid is neutralized. A color change in an acid–base indicator is used to determine when neutralization has occurred. The amount of basic solution added to achieve neutralization indicates the comparative strength of the acid. A basic solution is titrated in exactly the same way, except that an acid solution of known concentration is added.

Problem

How can the acidity or alkalinity of common household substances be determined?

Materials *(per group)*

3 different fruit juices   Use fruit juices with a pale color, avoiding juices that are red.
milk
4 liquid cleaning products   Use cleaners with a pale color.
antacid tablets, cut into quarters
white vinegar (5%)
safety goggles
stirring rod
4 test tubes
test-tube rack
medicine dropper
dropper bottle of
    phenolphthalein
graduated cylinder
test-tube brush

Procedure
Part A

1. Pour 5 mL of each fruit juice into its own test tube. Pour 5 mL of milk into a fourth test tube. Record the color of each liquid in Data Table 1.

2. Put four drops of phenolphthalein indicator into each test tube. Note the color of each juice and of the milk. Record your observations in Data Table 1.

© Prentice-Hall, Inc.

3. Add the quartered antacid tablets one at a time to one of the fruit juices, stirring after each quartered tablet is added. When a color change occurs, stop adding tablets to that test tube. Record your observations in Data Table 1.

4. Repeat the procedure for the remaining test tubes, making sure you wash off the stirring rod before proceeding to the next sample.

5. Wash the test tubes and stirring rod in preparation for performing Part B of the investigation.

Part B

1. Pour 5 mL of each liquid cleaning product into its own test tube. Record the color of each liquid in Data Table 2.

2. Put four drops of phenolphthalein indicator into each test tube. Note the color of each cleaning product. Record your observations in Data Table 2.

3. Add the vinegar one drop at a time to one of the cleaners, stirring after each drop is added. When a color change occurs, stop adding vinegar to that test tube. Record your observations in Data Table 2.

4. Repeat the procedure for the remaining test tubes, making sure you wash off the stirring rod before proceeding to the next sample.

5. Wash the test tubes and stirring rod thoroughly.

Observations

DATA TABLE 1

Liquid	Color	Color With Phenolphthalein	Number of Antacid Quarters Needed for Neutralization	Color After Neutralization
Juice				
Juice		Answers will vary.		
Juice				
Milk				

DATA TABLE 2

Cleaner	Color	Color With Phenolphthalein	Number of Vinegar Drops Needed for Neutralization	Color After Neutralization
		Answers will vary.		

Analysis and Conclusions

1. In what pH range (acid or basic) were the juices before neutralization?

   Below 7: acid.

   In what pH range was the milk? Below 7: acid.

2. Which of the beverages is probably the strongest acid? Answers will vary.

   Explain your conclusion. It needed the largest number of antacid tablets to change.

3. Which of your beverages is probably the weakest acid? Milk.

   Explain your conclusion. It needed the smallest number of antacid tablets to change.

4. List the four beverages in order of acidity from strongest to weakest.

   Answers will vary, but milk should be last.

5. In what pH range (acid or basic) were the cleaners before neutralization?

   Above 7: basic.

6. Which of your cleaners is probably the strongest base? Answers will vary.

   Explain your conclusion. It needed the largest number of vinegar drops to change.

7. Which of your cleaners is probably the weakest base? Answers will vary.

   Explain your conclusion. It needed the smallest number of vinegar drops to change.

8. List the four cleaners in order of alkalinity from strongest to weakest. Answers will vary.

Critical Thinking and Application

1. You may have found that the results you obtained were different from those of other groups. What variables might have affected your results in this investigation?

   Different antacids; different juices; variations in strengths of juices; cleanliness of test tubes.

   _____

   _____

2. What could you use to check the accuracy of your results in this investigation? Describe

   your procedure. Use pH paper or other acid–base indicator to check the pH of the substances

   used.

   _____

3. How could you determine the acidity or alkalinity of other substances found in your home? Write an investigation that you might do using pH paper as an indicator. Include the problem, hypothesis, materials, procedure, observations, and conclusions.

   Answers will vary.

   _____

   _____

   _____

   _____

   _____

   _____

   _____

   _____

Going Further

Obtain pH paper from your teacher and with his or her approval, perform the investigation you described above.

Laboratory Investigation

26

Fractional Distillation

You may want to refer students to pages 252–255 in the textbook for a general discussion of petroleum.

Time required: 45 minutes

Background Information

Fractional distillation is a process by which different liquids combined in a mixture can be separated on the basis of their different boiling points. During the process, the mixture is heated slowly so that each substance, or fraction, in the mixture reaches its boiling point and vaporizes. As it vaporizes, it leaves the liquid and passes to an area where it is cooled and condensed back to its liquid phase. The fraction is now separated from other substances in the mixture. Fractional distillation is used in the petroleum industry to separate crude oil into its many useful parts, which include gasoline, jet fuel, lubricants, and waxes.

In this investigation you will perform a fractional distillation of a mixture of water, isopropyl ("rubbing") alcohol, and ethylene glycol.

Problem

How can a mixture of liquids be separated by fractional distillation?

Materials (per group)

3 large test tubes
ring stand
test-tube clamp
test-tube rack
2-hole rubber stopper (to fit test tube)
400-mL beaker with crushed ice
several boiling chips
right-angle glass tubing
rubber tubing, 40 cm
Bunsen burner
Celsius thermometer
isopropyl alcohol   Prepare the mixture by mixing equal parts of
ethylene glycol   water, isopropyl alcohol, and ethylene glycol.
graph paper

Procedure

Caution students to shake the mixture before decanting as the liquids have different densities and will separate upon standing.

1. Half-fill a test tube with the liquid mixture provided by your teacher. Put the test tube in the test-tube rack while you set up the apparatus.

2. Set up the apparatus as shown in Figure 1. Note that the bulb of the thermometer is near the top of the test tube, not in the liquid. Place a few boiling chips in the test tube.

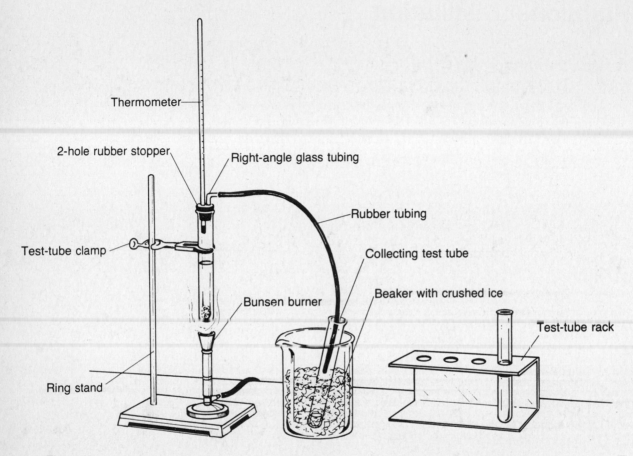

Thermometer

2-hole rubber stopper

Right-angle glass tubing

Rubber tubing

Test-tube clamp

Collecting test tube

Beaker with crushed ice

Bunsen burner

Test-tube rack

Ring stand

Figure 1

3. Light the Bunsen burner and slowly heat the test tube. Make sure that the flame is a moderate one. Do not allow the liquid to boil rapidly. Record the temperature at 1-minute intervals in the Data Table.

4. When the temperature stops rising, you should notice a liquid beginning to collect in the test tube in the beaker of crushed ice. Note this temperature in the Data Table.
   CAUTION: *Do not allow the rubber tubing to touch the liquid being collected.*
   If the tubing is below the liquid, the condensed liquid may be drawn back into the rubber tubing.

5. When the temperature begins rising again, remove the collecting test tube from the crushed ice and replace it with an empty test tube. Place the test tube with the collected liquid in the test-tube rack.

6. When the temperature again stops rising, you should notice a liquid beginning to collect in the test tube. Note this temperature in the Data Table. Do not allow the rubber tubing to touch the liquid being collected.

7. When the temperature begins rising again, turn off the Bunsen burner and allow the heated test tube to cool before taking apart the apparatus.

Observations

DATA TABLE These are sample data only. Actual data may vary.

Time (min)	1	2	3	4	5	6	7	8	9	10	11	12	13	14	15
Temperature (°C)	22	26	32	48	65	80	80	80	80	88	96	100	100	100	100

1. At what temperature did the first liquid fraction begin to collect in the cool test tube?

About 80°C.

2. At what temperature did the second liquid fraction begin to collect in the cool test

tube? About 100°C.

3. Describe the liquid remaining in the heated test tube.

Thick blue- or green-colored liquid.

4. Carefully smell the separated fractions and describe their odor.

First fraction smells like alcohol. Second fraction has no odor. Third fraction smells like alcohol.

Analysis and Conclusions

1. Draw a graph of your data. Plot time along the horizontal axis and temperature along the vertical axis.

2. On the basis of your observations of boiling temperature, odor, and appearance, identify

the three fractions. First is alcohol, second is water, and remaining is ethylene glycol.

3. Explain how each liquid was separated and then collected.

Each liquid fraction boils at a different temperature. The one with the lowest boiling point was vaporized

first, then cooled so that it condensed back to a liquid. The same thing occurred to the liquid with the

second-highest boiling point. The liquid remaining has the highest boiling point.

© Prentice-Hall, Inc.

Critical Thinking and Application

1. Did the complete separation of liquid fractions take place? _No._

   Explain. _Alcohol vapor was probably still in the test tube and tubing when the water started boiling._

   This alcohol would mix with the water.

   _____

   _____

2. Under what circumstances would it be more difficult to separate the fractions in a liquid

   mixture? _It would be more difficult if the boiling points of the fractions were closer together._

   _____

   _____

   _____

3. How do you know that fractional distillation is a physical separation, not a chemical

   one? _Boiling the liquids to vaporize them and then condensing them involves a change of phase, which_

   is a physical change.

   _____

   _____

Going Further

Solid substances can also be separated into useful components by a similar process called destructive distillation. Do library research to find out how destructive distillation is accomplished and what kinds of products result.

Laboratory Investigation

Chapter 10   Petrochemical Technology _____ **27** ____

Tensile Strength of Natural and Synthetic Polymers

You may want to refer students to pages 255–258 in the textbook for a general discussion of natural and synthetic polymers.

Time required: 40 minutes

Background Information

Tensile strength of a material is the amount of force required to break a wire or thread of that material. Tensile strength is a measure of the overall strength of the molecular forces that hold the substance together. Synthetic polymers such as polyester and nylon were developed to be stronger than natural polymers. In this investigation you will test the tensile strength of threads made of cotton (a natural polymer) and polyester, and you will draw conclusions as to which is stronger.

Problem

What are the tensile strengths of cotton, polyester, and cotton-covered polyester?

Materials (*per group*)

spring balance, 20-N capacity
polyester, cotton, and cotton-
  covered polyester threads of
  equal diameter
ring stand and ring
liquid bleach
3 beakers
cardboard
scissors
glass-marking pencil
safety goggles

Since tensile strength is a measure of force, this investigation utilizes the spring balance that measures force in newtons. However, students can use a spring balance that measures mass in grams in order to compare relative strengths of the materials in terms of how much mass they can hold before breaking.

Procedure

1. Obtain three beakers. Label the first beaker Polyester, the second beaker Cotton, and the third beaker Cotton-Covered Polyester.

2. Place three 40-cm-long pieces of polyester thread in the appropriate beaker. Repeat for the cotton and cotton-covered polyester threads.

3. Pour enough liquid bleach into each beaker to cover the bottom and the threads.

4. Set the beakers aside for 30 minutes.

5. Cut a piece of cardboard 1 cm × 5 cm. Fold the cardboard in half so that you have a V-shaped wedge that is 2.5 cm long.

6. Insert the legs of the cardboard wedge into the slot of the spring balance. See Figure 1.

7. Hang the top loop of the spring balance on the crossbar of the ring stand as shown in Figure 1.

8. Cut three 40-cm pieces of polyester threads. Tie loops on both ends for each of the three pieces.

9. Slip the loop of one end of one of the pieces of thread over the bottom hook of the spring balance. Slip a pencil or pen through the bottom loop.

10. Set the cardboard wedge to zero. Pull down very, very slowly on the pencil until the thread breaks.

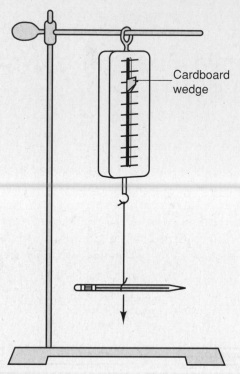

Cardboard wedge

Figure 1

11. Read the value on the scale that is opposite the top of the cardboard wedge. Record the tensile force to the nearest 0.1 N in the Data Table.

12. Obtain three trials for the polyester threads by repeating steps 9 through 11 two more times.

13. Repeat steps 8 through 12 for the cotton and then the cotton-covered polyester threads. Record all data.

14. After 30 minutes have elapsed, pour off the liquid bleach and rinse the beakers and threads several times with water. Dry the threads by pressing them between paper towels.

15. Now test these threads in the same way as before. Record your data in the Data Table.

Observations

DATA TABLE Possible answers

Trial	Without Bleach			With Bleach		
	1	2	3	1	2	3
Polyester	12.0	12.0	11.7	8.2	8.0	8.5
Cotton	8.0	8.5	8.2	2.2	2.0	2.5
Cotton-covered polyester	9.0	9.5	9.0	7.2	6.8	8.0

1. In the space below, calculate the average tensile force for the three trials for each material both without bleach and with bleach.
Possible answers

Without Bleach   With Bleach

Polyester: $\dfrac{12.0 + 12.0 + 11.7}{3} = 11.9$ N $\dfrac{8.2 + 8.0 + 8.5}{3} = 8.2$ N

Cotton: $\dfrac{8.0 + 8.5 + 8.2}{3} = 8.2$ N $\dfrac{2.2 + 2.0 + 2.5}{3} = 2.2$ N

Cotton covered: $\dfrac{9.0 + 9.5 + 9.0}{3} = 9.2$ N $\dfrac{7.2 + 6.8 + 8.0}{3} = 7.3$ N

2. How did the average values without bleach compare with the average values with bleach?

The values without bleach were higher than the values with bleach.

Analysis and Conclusions

1. Which material has the greatest tensile strength?

Polyester.

2. Which material loses the most tensile strength when soaked in bleach?

Cotton.

© Prentice-Hall, Inc.

Critical Thinking and Application

1. What general statement can you make about the effect of bleach on fibers?

Bleach weakens the fibers.

2. Parachutes, once made of the natural fiber silk, are today made of the synthetic polymer Dacron. What possible reason can you offer for this change?

Synthetic polymers are stronger than natural polymers. It would be important that a parachute be as strong as possible in order to support the weight of a human falling to the ground.

3. Which do you think would last longer, a shirt made of cotton or a shirt made of polyester? Explain your answer. Based on the strength of the fiber, the polyester shirt would last longer. However, other factors not tested in this investigation might favor the cotton.

4. The label in a 100-percent cotton dress reads, "Do not bleach." Why do you think this label is included? Cotton fibers lose a great deal of their strength when bleached. A manufacturer is concerned that the dress wear well, and so the caution against using bleach is included.

5. The most common thread used in materials is cotton-covered polyester. Is this thread used because of its high tensile strength? What other reasons could justify its widespread use? No. Polyester easily gets tangled and knotted. The cotton covering allows the thread to penetrate the cloth smoothly, while the polyester core adds strength.

Going Further

Test the tensile strength of nylon and wool. Using nylon and wool materials, repeat steps 8 through 15 of Procedure.

Laboratory Investigation

Chapter 11   Radioactive Elements

28

Half-Life of a Capacitor

You may want to refer students to pages 272–276 in the textbook for a general discussion of radioactive decay and half-life.

Time required: 40 minutes

Background Information

Radioactive material decays by emitting alpha or beta particles. During the process of decay, an atom of the original element decays into a different element. The time it takes for one half of all the atoms to decay into another element is called the half-life of the substance. Half-lives of elements can vary from microseconds to billions of years.

In this investigation you will determine the half-life of an electric capacitor. A capacitor stores a large quantity of electric charge and then slowly releases that charge. The same concept of radioactive half-life can be applied to a discharging capacitor. Unlike radioactive materials, capacitors do not give off radiation.

Problem

How do you determine the half-life of a discharging capacitor?

Materials (per group)

capacitor, 2000 to 6000
   microfarads
DC voltmeter   The voltage range of the voltmeter should be equal to or slightly greater than the power
pegboard   source. For example, if you use a 00–10-V voltmeter, use a 9.0-V power source.
DC power source
knife switch
connecting wires
clock with second hand   Mount the switch and capacitor on the pegboard. Be sure that the positive
                      terminal of the capacitor is connected to the positive terminal of the power
                      supply or the capacitor will be destroyed.

Procedure

1. Connect the capacitor, voltmeter, power source, and knife switch as shown in Figure 1.
   Note: *Make sure the positive terminal of the capacitor is connected to the positive terminal of the power source.*

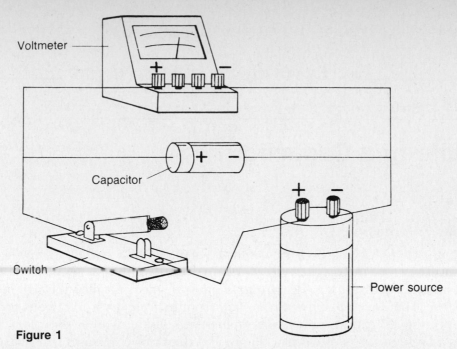

Voltmeter

Capacitor

Switch

Power source

Figure 1

2. Study the scale on the voltmeter carefully. Because you will have to read the voltage very quickly, notice what each division on the voltmeter scale represents.

3. One student in each group will be the timer. This student will watch the clock and will alert the others in the group to each 10-second interval. A second student will watch and read the voltmeter and call out its voltage at each 10-second interval. A third student will record the voltage in the proper 10-second interval in the Data Table.

Check student setups before allowing them to continue with step 4.

◄|⊢ **4. CAUTION:** *Be very careful when using electricity. Before your group closes the switch, have your teacher check your setup.* Close the switch and read the voltage. Do not start timing yet. Record this voltage in the Data Table next to 0 seconds.

DATA TABLE Answers will vary.

Time (sec)	Voltage (V)	Time (sec)	Voltage (V)	Time (sec)	Voltage (V)
0		80		160	
10		90		170	
20		100		180	
30		110		190	
40		120		200	
50		130		210	
60		140		220	
70		150		230	

5. Start timing the 10-second intervals the instant the switch is opened. During this time, the timer should call out "ten seconds," while the voltage reader tells what the voltage is. **Note:** *The student who reads the voltage should try to anticipate each 10-second interval. Otherwise, it may take more than 10 seconds to decide what the reading is.*

6. Continue taking readings until you are unable to read the amount of remaining voltage.

Observations

1. In Figure 2, draw a graph of your results. Place the time, in seconds, on the horizontal axis and the voltage on the vertical axis.

The larger the capacitance, the longer the half-life. A 0–12-V voltmeter and a 4600-microfarad capacitor yield a half-life of about 60 seconds. A 0–3-V voltmeter and a 6000-microfarad capacitor yield a half-life of about 100 seconds.

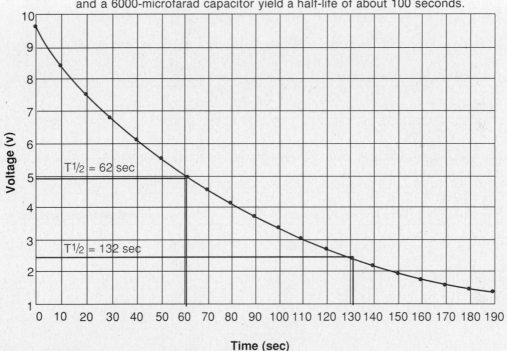

Figure 2

Analysis and Conclusions

1. Using the graph in Figure 2, find the half-life of the capacitor. To do so, find one half of the highest voltage on the vertical axis. For example, if the highest voltage is 10, one half of it is 5. Then move horizontally across from this point until you intersect your curve. Now vertically move down until you meet the horizontal axis. This is the time it takes for one half of the voltage to decay. What is this number?

Answers will vary.

2. How long did it take to reach one fourth of the original voltage?

Answers will vary.

© Prentice-Hall, Inc.

Critical Thinking and Application

1. If the original sample of a radioactive element were increased, what would happen to its half-life? Explain. The half-life would remain the same because it is independent of the size of the sample. It is a fixed rate of decay regardless of sample size.

2. After a period of four half-lives of a radioactive element has passed, what fraction of its original mass still remains? One sixteenth.

3. If an element gives off an alpha particle (helium nucleus) during radioactive decay, what happens to its atomic mass? Its atomic number? What happens to the atomic mass and atomic number of an element that gives off a beta particle (electron) during radioactive decay? During alpha decay, the atomic mass decreases by 4 and the atomic number decreases by 2. During beta decay, the atomic mass does not change and the atomic number increases by 1.

4. Why are elements with long half-lives used to date fossils of ancient plants and animals? By determining the ratio of original radioactive material to nonradioactive product, the number of half-lives the element has gone through can be calculated. The age of a fossil can be determined knowing how many half-lives have occurred and how many years each half-life is. Because fossils are very old, elements with long half-lives are more useful for dating because there will still be a measurable amount remaining.

Going Further

The half-life of the capacitor can be decreased by adding a resistor of at least 1000 ohms in parallel with the voltmeter. Determine the half-life of the capacitor when the resistor is added. If you want to increase the half-life of the capacitor, connect the resistor in series with the voltmeter.

_____ *Laboratory Investigation* _____

_____ **29** ____

Analyzing Motion

You may want to refer students to
pages 302–313 in their textbook for a
general discussion of speed, velocity,
and acceleration.

Time required: 2 40-minute periods

Background Information

Without complex and expensive instruments, it is difficult to obtain an accurate analysis
of the motion of an object. However, by graphing the distance vs. time of an object, it is
possible to determine at a glance whether an object is accelerating, decelerating, or moving
at a constant speed during a particular period of time.

A recording or acceleration timer is a simple device used to obtain quantitative
information about the motion of an object. During the operation of the timer, a moving
object pulls a piece of paper through the timer and under a hammer that strikes the paper
and records a series of dots. The more slowly the object moves, the closer together the dots.
The faster the object moves, the farther apart the dots. The distance between dots measures
the distance covered by the moving object in between two strikes of the hammer on the
paper. The time period between the strikes, which will be called a "tik," measures the time
it takes to go that distance.   Demonstrate the timer to students during pre-Lab discussion.

In this investigation you will use a recording timer to obtain information about a moving
object. You will then record that information on a graph and analyze and interpret the
results.

Problem

How can a graph be used to analyze the motion of an object?

Materials *(per group)*

recording (acceleration) timer   These materials are available from laboratory supply companies.
  with tape
Hall's carriage, skateboard, or
  roller skate
30-cm ruler
graph paper
masking tape
meterstick

Procedure   You may do this in your classroom if space permits. Otherwise use the hallway.

1. Set up the recording timer on the floor as demonstrated by your teacher.

2. Cut a length of recording tape 2 m long. Insert one end under the hammer of the timer
   and tape that end to the object you are using: cart, skateboard, or roller skate. The
   remaining tape should trail out behind in a straight line. See Figure 1.

3. While one lab partner starts the timer, another should give the skate a strong push across
   the floor away from the timer. Make sure that the skate pulls the tape completely
   through the timer. A third lab partner should be positioned to catch the moving object.

© Prentice-Hall, Inc.

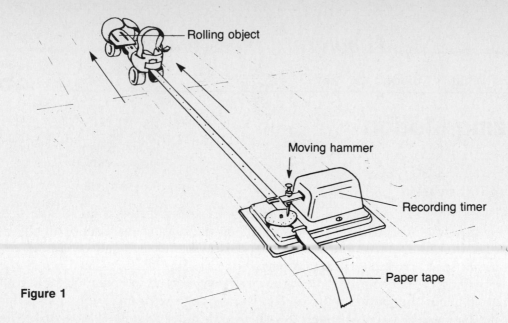

Rolling object

Moving hammer

Recording timer

Paper tape

Figure 1

4. Remove the tape from the object and mark the end that was attached to the skate "START." Move ahead 1 or 2 cm from here and mark this dot zero. Number every *second* dot after this 1, 2, 3, and so on. The numbers represent the time, measured in tiks, taken to travel the distance between the dots. This will give you the time information you need for your graph.

5. Using your 30-cm ruler, measure the distance to the nearest tenth of a centimeter between every set of numbers you placed on your tape. Record this information in the Data Table. This will give you the information about the distance your object traveled that you need for your graph.

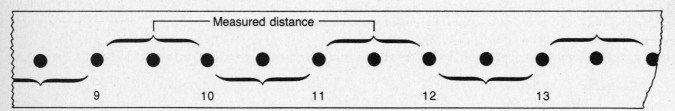

Measured distance

9   10   11   12   13

Figure 2

6. Draw a graph of the information you recorded in the Data Table. Plot time in tiks on the X axis and distance traveled in cm on the Y axis.

7. Using a colored pencil, draw a "curve of best fit" over your graph.

Observations

DATA TABLE

Interval	0 - 1 - 2 - 3 - 4 - 5 - 6 - 7 - 8 - 9 -10 -11 -12 -13 -14 -15 -16 -17 -18 -19 -20 -21 -22 -23 -24 - 25																								
Tik	1	2	3	4	5	6	7	8	9	10	11	12	13	14	15	16	17	18	19	20	21	22	23	24	25
Distance (cm)																									

Analysis and Conclusions

1. What were the units of time used in this investigation? Tiks. _____

   Why could seconds or minutes not be used? There is no way of knowing the actual speed of the

   timer.

   _____

   _____

2. How did the dots on the tape measure the speed at which the object moved?

   The slower the object moved, the closer the dots. The faster the object moved, the farther the dots.

   _____

   _____

   _____

3. Did your graph show that your object moved in a smooth, regular motion?

   Answers will vary, but probably not.

   Explain. Answers will vary but might include: the floor wasn't smooth; the wheels weren't round.

   _____

   _____

   _____

4. Why was it necessary to draw a "curve of best fit?"

   Because the graph was not smooth and regular, it was necessary to "smooth it out" to get a better idea

   of how the object moved.

   _____

   _____

5. Examine your "curve of best fit." Was your object accelerating, decelerating, or traveling

   at constant speed? Answers will vary.

   _____

   _____

   _____

© Prentice-Hall, Inc.

Critical Thinking and Application

1. Calculate the average velocity in cm/tik of the object. Find the difference between the fastest velocity and the slowest velocity and divide the result by 2.

Answers will vary.

2. Does the average velocity that you calculated tell how fast the object was really going at any instant of time? No.

Explain your answer. At any given instant the speed was somewhere between the highest and lowest speeds.

3. What are some variables that might have prevented your graph from being smooth like the "curve of best fit"? Answers may include: uneven floor, uneven wheels, obstructions on floor, inaccurate measurement.

Going Further

Use the recording timer to investigate the motion of falling objects. Place the timer at the top of a high shelf or cabinet and drop a mass attached to the recording tape to the floor. Record your data and draw a graph. Compare your results with the motion of the rolling object.

Laboratory Investigation

Chapter 12   What Is Motion? _____ **30** ___

Calculating Acceleration

You may want to refer students to pages 309–313 in their textbook for a general discussion of velocity and acceleration.

Background Information

Time required: 40 minutes

Acceleration is the rate of change of velocity. Suppose a car accelerates from rest to 10 m/sec in 5 sec. Its acceleration is: $\dfrac{10\text{ m/sec} - 0\text{ m/sec}}{5\text{ sec}} = 2$ m/sec/sec. In this investigation you will determine the acceleration of a moving object.

You may point out that 10 m/sec equals 10 meters per second.

Problem

How is the acceleration of a moving object calculated?

Materials _(per group)_

bicycle
2 stopwatches
masking tape
meterstick

Procedure

1. Find a level surface suitable for riding a bicycle.

2. Place a piece of masking tape on the ground at the starting point.

3. Using a meterstick, measure 20 m from the first tape. Mark the 20-m distance with another piece of masking tape.

4. Place a third piece of tape 5 m past the 20-m tape. Your tapes should look like Figure 1.

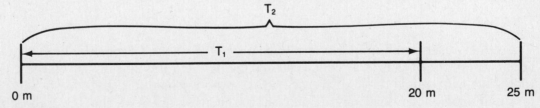

0 m   T₁   20 m   25 m

Figure 1

5. The bicycle will start at the zero meter mark.

6. Have one person stand with stopwatch 1 at the 20-m mark. Have another member of your group stand with stopwatch 2 at the 25-m mark.

7. One person will act as the starter. When the starter says "go," begin riding the bicycle. At the same time, have your classmates start both stopwatches.

© Prentice-Hall, Inc.

8. Stopwatch 1 will record the time (T_1) it takes for the bicycle to reach the 20-m mark. Stopwatch 2 will time the full 25 m (T_2).

9. Try several practice runs.

10. When you obtain consistent time results, take three time trials and record the times in the Data Table.

Observations

DATA TABLE (possible answers)

Trial	T_1 (sec)	T_2 (sec)
1	4.8	5.4
2	4.7	5.0
3	4.9	5.5

1. Calculate the time it took the bicycle to move from the 20-m mark to the 25-m mark for each trial (T_v). $T_v = T_2 - T_1$.

    Trial 1   5.4 sec − 4.8 sec = 0.6 sec
    Trial 2   5.3 sec − 4.7 sec = 0.6 sec
    Trial 3   5.5 sec − 4.9 sec = 0.6 sec

2. Calculate the velocity (v_1) between the 20-m mark and 25-m mark for each trial.

    $$\text{Velocity} = \frac{5m}{T_v}$$

    Trial 1 $\dfrac{5.0 \text{ m}}{0.6 \text{ sec}}$ = 8.3 m/sec

    Trial 2 $\dfrac{5.0 \text{ m}}{0.6 \text{ sec}}$ = 8.3 m/sec

    Trial 3 $\dfrac{5.0 \text{ m}}{0.6 \text{ sec}}$ = 8.3 m/sec

3. The velocity calculated in question 2 was an average velocity. Since the bicycle was accelerating, the velocity was continually changing from the 20-m mark to the 25-m mark. We will assume that the average velocity you calculated is the same as the instantaneous velocity halfway between the two marks. The total time (T_t), therefore, should be T_1 plus one-half of T_v. Calculate T_t for each trial. $T_t = T_1 + \frac{1}{2}T_v$.

    Trial 1   4.8 sec + $\dfrac{0.6 \text{ sec}}{2}$ = 5.1 sec

    Trial 2   4.7 sec + $\dfrac{0.6 \text{ sec}}{2}$ = 5.0 sec

    Trial 3   4.9 sec + $\dfrac{0.6 \text{ sec}}{2}$ = 5.2 sec

Analysis and Conclusions

1. Calculate the acceleration of the bicycle for each trial. Acceleration = $\dfrac{V_1 - V_0}{T_t}$
   Remember: Since the bicycle started from rest, V_0 is 0 m/sec.

Trial 1 $\dfrac{8.3 \text{ m/sec} - 0 \text{ m/sec}}{5.1 \text{ sec}} = 1.6 \text{ m/sec/sec}$

Trial 2 $\dfrac{8.3 \text{ m/sec} - 0 \text{ m/sec}}{5.0 \text{ sec}} = 1.7 \text{ m/sec/sec}$

Trial 3 $\dfrac{8.3 \text{ m/sec} - 0 \text{ m/sec}}{5.2 \text{ sec}} = 1.6 \text{ m/sec/sec}$

2. Based on this investigation, what measurements must be made in order to calculate the acceleration of an object that begins at rest?

   Distance traveled, time, average final velocity.

Critical Thinking and Application

1. What hidden variable in this investigation might make it difficult to obtain consistent

   results in the three trials? The amount of force used by the rider as he or she starts pedaling the

   bike.

2. Can acceleration ever be negative? Explain your answer.

   Yes, if the final velocity is less than the initial velocity. An example would be applying the brakes to a

   moving car to bring it to a stop.

3. Suppose you wanted to determine the acceleration of a ball rolled along a flat surface. What factor might make this calculation more difficult than determining the acceleration

   of a bicycle? Unlike the bike, the ball has no source of energy to keep it going. Soon after the ball is

   rolled, friction will begin to slow it down.

© Prentice-Hall, Inc.

4. Suppose the acceleration of a bicycle were calculated as zero. Assuming the bicycle is not at rest, what must be true about its motion?

It must be traveling at a constant velocity.

Going Further

What is the acceleration of an object that takes 7 sec to change its velocity from 25 m/sec to 39 m/sec?

$$\text{Acceleration} = \frac{39 \text{ m/sec} - 25 \text{ m/sec}}{7 \text{ sec}} = \frac{14 \text{ m/sec}}{7 \text{ sec}} = 2 \text{ m/sec/sec}$$

_____ *Laboratory Investigation* _____

Construction and Use of an Accelerometer

You may want to refer students to pages 309–313 in their textbook for a general discussion of velocity and acceleration.

Time required: 40 minutes

Background Information

A device called an accelerometer is often used for measuring acceleration. Acceleration is a change in the rate of velocity of an object. Since velocity involves both speed and direction, acceleration measurements can be of speed or direction. In this investigation you will construct an accelerometer and use it to determine the direction of acceleration.

Problem

How is the direction of acceleration determined by an accelerometer?

Materials *(per group)*

1-l jar with lid
string
lead sinker or large machine nut
candle
matches

Procedure

1. Tie the lead sinker to a piece of string.

2. Cut the string so that it is slightly shorter than the length of the jar.

3. Attach the free end of the string to the center of the bottom of the lid using melted candle wax.

4. Allow the candle wax to completely harden. Test to see if the wax holds the string and sinker. If it does not, add more candle wax to the point of attachment.

5. Completely fill the jar with water.

6. Place the sinker in the water and tightly screw on the lid. Your accelerometer should look like the one in Figure 1.

Figure 1

7. Hold the jar steady and start walking. Record the position of the sinker as you accelerate and as you walk at a constant speed.

8. Record the position of the sinker as you stop.

9. Walk around in a circle about 1 m in diameter. Record the sinker positions.

© Prentice-Hall, Inc.

Observations

1. What is the direction of the sinker as you accelerate from rest?

   The sinker moves backward.

2. What is the direction of the sinker when you are walking at a constant speed in a straight line?

   The sinker remains in the vertical, or rest, position.

3. What is the position of the sinker when you are walking at a constant speed in a circle?

   The sinker points outward from the center of the circle.

Analysis and Conclusions

1. When you accelerate, does the sinker move backward or does the bottle move forward?

   The bottle moves forward.

2. Does the sinker point toward or away from the direction of acceleration?

   The sinker points away from the direction of acceleration.

3. Based on your observations, how does the rate at which your speed changes affect the position of the sinker?

   The faster you move, the more the sinker moves.

Critical Thinking and Application

1. What would happen if you accelerated the bottle downward? Upward?

   If the bottle accelerates downward, the sinker will lag behind causing the string to bunch up. If the bottle

   accelerates upward, the sinker will also lag behind, pulling on the string and possibly breaking it.

142

2. How do the movements of the sinker relate to your movements when you are traveling in a bus?

Your body experiences the same movements as the sinker. You move back into your seat when the bus

accelerates. You jerk forward when the bus stops. You fall toward the windows when the bus rounds a

corner.

3. There is a circular ride in most amusement parks called a spinner. The people who ride on it stand up around the walls while it spins rapidly. As the ride continues, the floor drops out, but the people remain where they are. Analyze the motion of the people in relation to your observations of the motion of the sinker.

Just as the sinker moves outward from the center of the circle, so too do the people. However, unlike the

sinker which is held in place by its attachment to the lid, the people are held in place by a wall.

Going Further

Hold your accelerometer while sitting in a car. Observe the position of the sinker as the car accelerates, moves at a constant speed, stops, and turns corners.

© Prentice-Hall, Inc.

Laboratory Investigation

Chapter 13 The Nature of Forces

32

Investigating Friction

You may want to refer students to pages 326–328 in their textbook for a general discussion of the force of friction.

Time required: 40 minutes

Background Information

One of the forces you have studied is friction. Friction is a retarding force. This means it lessens the effect of other forces. Friction, therefore, causes a "loss" of useful energy in many mechanical devices. This energy, of course, is not really lost but is transferred to heat energy at the point of contact.

In this investigation you will explain why the movement of one object over another produces heat and how changes in design can reduce friction. You will also learn how surface area, texture, and weight influence friction.

Problem

What are some factors that affect friction?

Materials *(per group)*

spring balance
rectangular block of wood fitted
    with a metal eye
large piece of sandpaper

Procedure

1. Suspend a block of wood from the spring balance and obtain its weight in newtons. Record the weight below.

   Weight of block _____

2. Place the block on the lab table with its larger surface (side A) downward. See Figure 1.

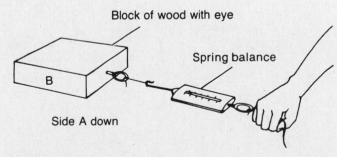

Block of wood with eye

Spring balance

B

Side A down

Figure 1

3. Keep the spring scale level with the table and pull the block along the table. In Data Table 1 record the force indicated on the spring scale needed to start the block moving. Also record the force indicated on the spring scale once the block is sliding evenly along the lab table.

4. Repeat step 3 twice, recording your readings in Data Table 1. Calculate the average for the starting friction and the sliding friction.

5. Calculate the surface area for side A (area = length × width), and record it in the space provided.

6. Place the block on the lab table with its smaller surface (side B) downward. See Figure 2.

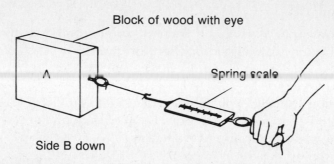

Block of wood with eye

Spring scale

Side B down

Figure 2

7. Repeat steps 3 and 4. Record your readings in Data Table 1.

8. Calculate the area for side B and record it in the space provided.

9. Repeat steps 1 through 8, sliding the surfaces of the block over a piece of sandpaper. Record your readings in Data Table 2 for side A and for side B.

10. Obtain a block of wood from a classmate, along with the data on its weight. Place it on top of your block so that the original A side is facing down. Record the weight of the two blocks and the sliding force required to move them across the lab table.

Weight of two blocks _____ Average sliding force _____

If time permits, borrow a third block and repeat.

Weight of three blocks _____ Average sliding force _____

Observations

DATA TABLE 1

Surface Area of Side A _____ cm²

Trial	Starting Friction (N)	Sliding Friction (N)
1		
2		
3		
Average		

Surface Area of Side B _____ cm²

Trial	Starting Friction (N)	Sliding Friction (N)
1		
2		
3		
Average		

DATA TABLE 2

Side A

Trial	Starting Friction (N)	Sliding Friction (N)
1		
2		
3		
Average		

Side B

Trial	Starting Friction (N)	Sliding Friction (N)
1		
2		
3		
Average		

How did the starting friction compare to the sliding friction?

The starting friction was greater. _____

Analysis and Conclusions

1. What do you think accounts for the difference between the starting friction and the sliding friction?

   Inertia had to be overcome. _____

   _____

2. Based on your data, how does the surface area influence the sliding force of friction?

   As the surface area increases, so does the force of friction.

   _____

   _____

3. Based on your data, how does texture influence the sliding force of friction?

   A rougher texture will increase the force of friction.

   _____

   _____

4. How does weight influence the sliding force of friction?

   The weight increases the pressure on the contact surface. The force of friction increases.

   _____

© Prentice-Hall, Inc.

Critical Thinking and Application

1. List two situations in which friction can be helpful.

   Answers will vary but might include brakes on a car, nonslip bath mats, rubber soles on boots.

2. List two ways you could reduce the friction between two or more surfaces.

   Decrease contact area, smooth the surfaces, decrease pressure, use a lubricant.

3. Why do wheels reduce the force of friction? They provide a smoother surface and reduce the

   contact area.

4. Which task would require more effort, pushing a 1-kg box across an ordinary floor or pushing a 2000-kg box across a frictionless floor? Explain your answer.

   Pushing the 1-kg box across an ordinary floor because it is the force of friction that acts against motion.

   Pushing even the largest box on a frictionless surface would require very little effort—perhaps a slight

   push to get the box moving.

Going Further

1. Determine the advantages of lubricants such as grease and oil by performing a similar experiment.

2. Determine what happens to automobile motor oil when the engine heats up. Why is it important to have a heavier oil in summer than in winter?

Laboratory Investigation

Chapter 13   The Nature of Forces

33

Determining Acceleration Due to Gravity

You may want to refer students to pages 335–342 in their textbook for a general discussion of acceleration due to gravity.

Time required: Part A—20 minutes
　　　　　　　Part B—20 minutes

Background Information

If air resistance is small, the rate at which a body falls is constant, regardless of its mass. The rate at which a body falls is determined by the gravitational force exerted on the body. On the surface of the Earth, acceleration due to gravity is close to 9.8 m/sec^2. In this investigation you will determine acceleration due to gravity using two different methods.

Problem

How can acceleration due to gravity near the surface of the Earth be determined?

Materials *(per group)*

string or wire about 1.5 m long

A weight or heavy objects such as books can be placed on the base of the ring stand to steady it.

hooked weight, 500 g

timer

buret

pie plate

meterstick

beaker

ring stand with buret clamp

If burets are not available, use anything that can control the rate of drip. A container with spigot works well.

Procedure

Part A   Measuring Acceleration Due to Gravity Using a Pendulum

1. Place the ring stand on a table so that the clamp hangs over the side of the table. See Figure 1. Tie one end of the string to the clamp. Attach the 500-g weight to the other end of the string.

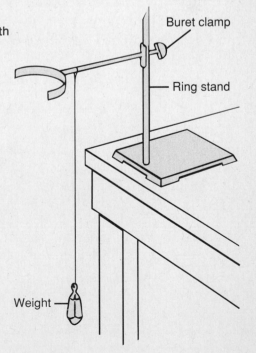

Buret clamp

Ring stand

Weight

Figure 1

2. Pull the weight back about ten degrees from its rest position. Release the weight and record in Data Table 1 the time (T) in seconds it takes to make 20 complete swings. One complete swing is back and forth.

DATA TABLE 1

Length (L) (m)	Time (T) 20 swings (sec)
1.5 m (Approximate answers)	50 sec

3. Measure the length (L) of the wire or string from the center of the weight to the ring stand. Record this length to the nearest 0.01 m in the Data Table.

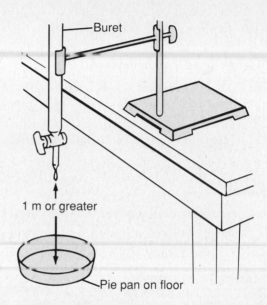

Part B Measuring the Acceleration of a Water Drop

1. Attach the buret to the ring stand with the buret clamp. See Figure 2. Fill the buret about three fourths full of water.

2. Place the pie pan on the floor beneath the buret. The pie pan should be at least 1 m below the base of the buret.

3. Adjust the drip rate so that one drop just leaves the buret when the previous drop hits the pie pan. Watch the drop at the buret and listen for the sound.

Figure 2

4. After adjusting the drip rate, record in Data Table 2 the number of seconds it takes for 100 drops to hit the pie plate. Keep the level of the water in the buret approximately constant by refilling it with a beaker.

DATA TABLE 2

Distance (d) (m)	Time (T) 100 drops (sec)
1.0 m (Possible answers)	46 sec

5. Measure the distance (d) from the tip of the buret to the pie plate. Record this distance to the nearest 0.01 m in the Data Table.

Observations
Part A

1. Calculate the time (T) for a single swing. (Divide the time for 20 swings by 20.)

$$\frac{50 \text{ sec}}{20} = 2.5 \text{ sec}$$

2. Calculate the acceleration due to gravity in m/sec² using the formula:

$$A_G = \frac{39.5 \cdot L}{T^2}$$

where A_G = acceleration of gravity, L = length in meters, and T = time in seconds for one swing.

$$A_G = \frac{(39.5 \times 1.5 \text{ m})}{(2.5 \text{ sec})^2} = 9.5 \text{ m/sec}^2$$

Part B

3. Calculate the time (T) for a single water drop to fall. (Divide the time for 100 drops by 100.)

$$\frac{46 \text{ sec}}{100} = 0.46 \text{ sec}$$

4. Calculate the acceleration due to gravity using the formula:

$$A_G = \frac{2D}{T^2}$$

where A_G = acceleration of gravity, D = distance in meters, and T = time in seconds for one drop.

$$A_G = \frac{2(1.0 \text{ m})}{(0.46 \text{ sec})^2} = 9.5 \text{ m/sec}^2$$

Analysis and Conclusions

1. The acceleration of gravity is approximately 9.8 m/sec². Which method was more

accurate? Answers will vary. _____

2. Can you offer possible reasons for your answer to question 1?

Answers will vary, but should reflect potential inaccuracies in measurement during either Part A or

Part B. _____

_____

_____

_____

_____

© Prentice-Hall, Inc.

Critical Thinking and Application

1. Compare the motion of the object in Part A with the motion of the water droplets in Part B. How did the force of gravity influence each one?

   The object in Part A moved in an arc, falling down and then swinging back up. It was the force of gravity

   that pulled the object down to the low point of its arc each time. The water droplets fell to the ground in a

   straight line. It was the force of gravity that caused them to fall.

2. Study the formula used to calculate acceleration due to gravity in Part A. Assuming that A_G is constant, what must be true about the relationship between the length of the string and the time it takes for the pendulum to make one complete swing?

   The square of the time increases as the length of the string increases.

3. Suppose you performed Part A using strings of varying lengths. How would you expect your calculated value of A_G to compare with the results you obtained in this investigation?

   Should be the same.

4. Study the formula you used to calculate acceleration due to gravity in Part B. How is the time taken for one droplet to fall related to the distance it falls?

   The square of the time increases as the distance increases.

Going Further

1. Perform Part A again, but this time attach a feather to the string instead of a weight.

   How does that affect your results? Why? Results no longer valid because of effects of air
   resistance on feather.

2. Perform Part B again, but this time use vegetable oil instead of water. How does that affect your results? No change.

   Note: A container with a spigot will be easier to clean out than a buret.

_____ *Laboratory Investigation* _____

34 ___

Weight and the Force of Gravity

You may want to refer students to pages 335–342 in their textbook for a general discussion of weight and the force of gravity.

Time required: Part A—20 minutes
Part B—15 minutes

Background Information

There is a difference between mass and weight. The mass of an object is defined as the amount of matter it contains. The weight of an object is determined by the force of gravity on its mass.

You have used a triple-beam balance to measure mass. To measure weight, a spring balance is used. Because weight is the downward force that results from the pull of gravity on an object, when a weight is attached to a spring the downward force will stretch the spring. The greater the weight of the object, the more the spring stretches.

If known masses are attached to a spring, the amount of stretch (weight) caused by different masses can be determined.

In this investigation you will measure how much a spring stretches as weight is applied to it. You will then determine the relationship between mass and weight.

Problem

How can a spring be used to measure the force known as weight?

Materials *(per group)*

ring stand
large ring
meterstick
clamp
spring

15 washers
2 large paper clips (washer hooks)
100-g mass

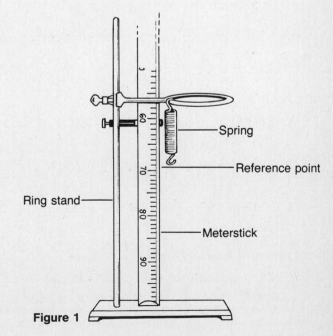

Spring

Reference point

Ring stand

Meterstick

Figure 1

Procedure
Part A

1. Attach the ring to the ring stand and hang the spring from it.

2. Clamp the meterstick to the ring stand so that the 100-cm mark is resting on the table top and the spring is close to, but not touching, the meterstick. Attach the washer hook to the bottom of the spring. See Figure 1.

© Prentice-Hall, Inc.

3. Note the number on the meterstick, to the nearest tenth of a centimeter, that is just even with the bottom of the spring. This number will be your reference point. Record this number in the Data Table.

4. Attach five washers to the washer hook and note the number on the meterstick that is just even with the bottom of the spring now. Record this number in the Data Table.

5. Repeat step 4 with 10 washers and then 15 washers added to the hook.

6. Remove the washers *five at a time* until no washers remain. Each time you remove five washers, note the number on the meterstick that is just even with the bottom of the spring. Record.

Part B

1. Note the reference point again. Record in Observations for Part B.

2. Hang a 100-g mass from the spring and note the number on the meterstick that is just even with the bottom of the spring. Record this number in Observations for Part B.

Observations
Part A

DATA TABLE

Number of Washers	Reading of Meterstick	Change in Length of Spring
0		
5	Answers will vary.	
10		
15		
10		
5		
0		

Part B

1. Reference point <u>Answers will vary.</u> cm

2. Meterstick reading with 100-g mass <u>Answers will vary.</u>

3. Change in length of spring <u>Answers will vary.</u>

Analysis and Conclusions

1. Draw a graph of your results in the Data Table. Label the vertical axis "Stretch (cm)" and the horizontal axis "Number of washers."

2. How much did the length of the spring change as each group of five washers was

added? Answers will vary. _____

3. How much did the length of the spring change as each group of five washers was

removed? Answers will vary. _____

4. How do your answers to questions 2 and 3 compare? They are the same. _____

Explain. The increase in length as five washers are added is equal to the decrease in length as those

same five washers are removed. The weight of those washers is the same, and that is what the spring

measures.

_____

5. How does the shape of your graph illustrate your answers to questions 2 and 3?

The graph is a straight line. This shows that the stretch increased and decreased by the same amount

each time as the same number of washers was added.

_____

_____

Critical Thinking and Application

1. What force acts on the objects you attached to the spring? Gravity. _____

2. In terms of forces, explain why the spring stretched as more washers were added.

There was a larger mass so the force of gravity increased.

_____

_____

_____

3. In Part B you added a known mass to the spring. Since you know the amount by which
this known mass stretched the spring, calculate the mass of five washers.

You may need to discuss the method of calculation.
Answers will vary. _____

What is the mass of one washer? Answers will vary. _____

4. Why do spring balances vary in accuracy? They do not always stretch by the same amount when weights are added. They may be affected by temperature and/or humidity.

5. How is the maximum capacity of a spring balance determined?

The maximum capacity is the point at which it does not return to its original shape when weights are removed. It exceeds its "elastic limit."

Going Further

Use the results obtained in Part B to calculate the masses of other objects. Verify your results by finding their mass on a balance. If your results differ, which do you think is more accurate, the balance or the spring? Explain.

Laboratory Investigation

35

Finding the Center of Gravity

You may want to refer students to pages 335–342 in their textbook for a general discussion of gravity and motion.

Time required: 40 minutes

Background Information

You should remember the difference between mass and weight. The mass of an object is defined as the amount of matter it contains. The weight of an object is determined by the force of gravity on the object. Because an object has mass, the Earth has an attraction for it. This force of attraction is called gravity. Gravitational force gives the object weight.

Regardless of the size and shape of an object, its weight seems to be concentrated at one point. This point is called the center of gravity. It is as if the force of attraction between the Earth and the object were acting at this one point alone.

In this investigation you will determine the center of gravity of an irregularly shaped object.

Problem

How can the center of gravity of an irregularly shaped, flat object be determined?

Materials (per group)

cardboard square (about 30 cm ×
   30 cm)
scissors
ruler
hole puncher
small metal weight or heavy
   washer
string (about 40 cm)
pencil
pegboard attached to wall
pegboard hook

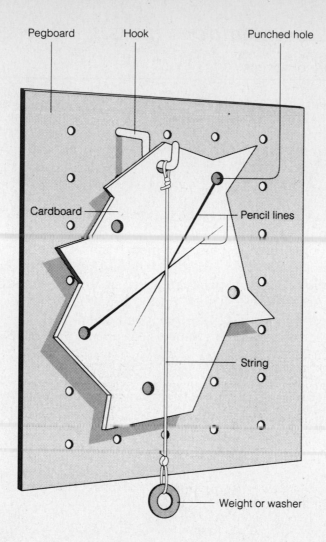

Labels on figure: Pegboard, Hook, Punched hole, Cardboard, Pencil lines, String, Weight or washer

Figure 1

Procedure

1. Cut the cardboard square into an irregular shape. Punch at least five holes around its edge.

2. Hang the cardboard from the pegboard hook by passing the hook through one of the punched holes. The diameter of the holes must be larger than that of the hook so that the cardboard hangs freely.

3. Attach the weight or washer to the string. Hang the string from the hook so that it hangs straight down and freely in front of the cardboard. Use the ruler and pencil to mark on the cardboard the straight line made by the string.

4. Repeat steps 2 and 3 until you have hung the cardboard from each of its holes.

Observations

Describe the appearance of the lines on the cardboard.

The lines intersect at one point.

In the space below draw a sketch of your cardboard after you have completed the Procedure.

```
┌─────────────────────────────────────┐
│                                     │
│                                     │
│                                     │
│                                     │
│                                     │
│                                     │
│                                     │
└─────────────────────────────────────┘
```

Analysis and Conclusions

1. Where is the center of gravity of the cardboard? Why is this point the center of gravity?

The center of gravity is at the point at which the lines intersect. Each line drawn represents the line of

force of gravity for each position of the cardboard. The point of intersection is the common point of

gravitational force.

_____

2. Try to balance the cardboard on the end of your finger. At what point does the object

balance? At the center of gravity.

Why? An object can be balanced if its center of gravity is supported.

_____

3. Could the method used in this investigation also be used to determine the center of

gravity of a regularly shaped object? Yes.

Critical Thinking and Application

1. The center of gravity is sometimes called the center of mass. Explain why these terms are

interchangeable. On the Earth, mass and weight can be considered interchangeable. Because an

object has mass, it will experience gravitational force. The point at which all of the object's mass seems

to be concentrated will be the point at which all of the gravitational force seems to be acting.

_____

© Prentice-Hall, Inc.

2. A tightrope walker will fall if he leans too far over to one side. Relate this to the concept of the center of gravity. The tightrope walker balances by keeping his center of gravity over the rope. When he leans over he moves his center of gravity.

3. You can probably bend over and touch your toes without bending your knees. However, you could not do this exercise if your heels and back are against a wall. Try it. Explain this in terms of the center of gravity. Students will fall over if they try to touch their toes when their heels and back are against the wall. This is because they will not be able to maintain their center of gravity over their feet.

Going Further

Repeat this activity using a ring-shaped piece of cardboard that has a large hole at the center. Does there actually need to be any matter at the center of mass of an object?

Laboratory Investigation

36

Relating Archimedes' Principle of Buoyancy

You may want to refer students to pages 358–361 in their textbook for a general discussion of buoyancy.

Time required: 40 minutes

Background Information

Fluids exert a pressure in all directions. The force that pushes upward in a fluid is called buoyancy. The upward buoyant force of a fluid opposes the downward force of gravity on an object placed in the fluid. According to Archimedes' principle, the buoyancy of an object equals the weight of the fluid the object displaces.

Weight and mass are not the same thing. It happens, however, that it is more convenient to test Archimedes' principle in the laboratory using measurements of mass rather than measurements of weight. The buoyancy of an object can be determined in terms of the mass of water the object displaces. This method works because mass and weight are proportional anywhere on the Earth.

If a solid piece of metal is placed in water, the metal will displace a volume of water equal to the metal's own volume. One milliliter of water has a mass of 1 g. So the volume of water displaced equals the mass of the water displaced. And the mass of water displaced equals the volume of the object. The buoyancy of the object in water, therefore, is the same value as the volume of the object.

An object placed in water appears to lose mass. This apparent loss in mass is equal to the mass of the displaced water, or the volume of the object. So a 100-g object that has a volume of 25 mL will have an apparent mass of 75 g (100 − 25) when placed in water.

In this investigation you will determine the mass of a metal object in air. Then you will suspend the object in water and determine the mass again. You will then compare the apparent loss in mass with the volume of the displaced water.

Problem

How does buoyancy relate to the apparent loss of mass of an object?

Materials (*per group*)

centigram balance
25-mL graduated cylinder
100-mL beaker
metal object   A fishing line sinker works well since it is easily attached to the thread.
thread
ring stand with support ring
wire gauze

Procedure

1. Tie the metal object to the thread. Suspend the object in air by tying the thread to the hook above the balance pan of the centigram balance. Record the mass of the object to the nearest 0.1 g in the Data Table.

2. Set up the ring stand and support ring covered with wire gauze next to the balance so that a beaker may be placed under the metal object.

3. Half-fill the beaker with water. Set up the metal object, thread, and beaker of water as shown in Figure 1. Do not remove or touch the balance pan.

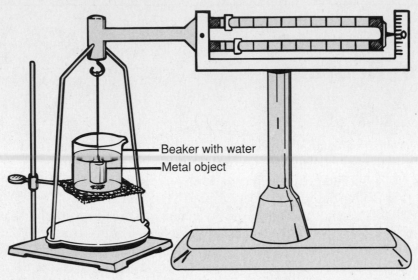

Beaker with water
Metal object

Figure 1

4. Make sure the metal object is completely submerged in the water and is not touching the sides or bottom of the beaker.

5. Record the mass of the object in water to the nearest 0.1 g.

6. Place about 10 mL of water in the graduated cylinder. Record the volume to the nearest 0.1 mL.

7. Carefully place the metal object in the graduated cylinder. Record the new volume of the water to the nearest 0.1 mL.

Observations

Note: Figures in the Data Table and ''Observations'' and ''Analysis and Conclusions'' are possible answers. Students' numbers will vary, but the procedure remains the same.

DATA TABLE

Mass of object in air	12.5 g
Mass of object in water	8.4 g
Volume of water before adding object	10.0 mL
Volume of water after adding object	14.0 mL

1. Determine the loss of mass (buoyancy) of the object (mass in air − mass in water).

12.5 g − 8.4 g = 4.1 g

2. Determine the volume of water displaced by the object.

14.0 mL − 10.0 mL = 4.0 mL

3. Determine the mass of water displaced. Hint: 1 g of water = 1 mL of water.

4.0 mL = 4.0 g

Analysis and Conclusions

1. Is the buoyancy of the object about the same as the mass of water displaced?

Yes; 4.1 g ≈ 4.0 g

2. Why is the loss of mass of the object only an apparent loss?

An object can never gain or lose mass.

Critical Thinking and Application

1. A dancer finds that it is easier to lift a leg while standing in a swimming pool than while

standing on the floor. Why? The buoyant force of the water supports some of the weight of the leg,

making it "lighter." Thus it is easier to lift.

2. People undergoing physical therapy after an injury often find it helpful to perform

exercises in water. Why? Because of the buoyant force of the water, it takes less effort to support

and move one's body weight. Thus the injured person would find it less stressful to exercise in water.

3. Explain why it is important in this investigation that the metal object not be touching the

bottom or sides of the beaker. Some of the metal's mass would be supported by the beaker, rather

than just by the water.

© Prentice-Hall, Inc.

4. Suppose two blocks of identical shape and size were placed in water. Block A is made of wood and block B is made of iron. How would the buoyant force on these two objects compare? Why? Assume both blocks sink below the water line.

Both buoyant forces would be the same, since the volume of water displaced would be the same in both cases.

5. Explain what happens when a swimmer floats.

The buoyant force of the water supports enough of the swimmer's body weight to keep the swimmer from sinking.

Going Further

Put some water and ice in a glass, and mark the level of the top of the water on the side of the glass. When the ice melts, observe whether the level of the top of the water is higher, lower, or the same as before. Discuss your observation with your classmates and teacher.

Laboratory Investigation _____

Chapter 15   Work, Power, and Simple Machines   **37** ____

Can You Work More Efficiently?

You may want to refer students to pages 377–380 in their textbook for a general discussion of simple machines and efficiency.

Time required: 35 minutes

Background Information

Work is applying a force to an object to move the object a certain distance in the direction of the force. If you pick up a book, you are doing work because you are exerting an upward force and moving an object in the same direction.

By using a simple machine, you can make work easier. For certain tasks, you can make work easier by decreasing the effort force required to move a resistance force. In other words, a smaller effort force can be applied to move a heavy mass. This is the concept of mechanical advantage.

In this investigation you will see how the mechanical advantage of a simple machine can be changed to enable you to work more efficiently.

Problem

Can the mechanical advantage of a simple machine be altered?

Materials _(per group)_

heavy string, 65 cm long
4 thin wooden rods: 1, 7 cm long; 2, 14 cm long; 1, 20 cm long

Pencils of different lengths can be used as long as there are two long pencils.

book
2 tables or desks to serve as supports
watch or clock with second hand

Procedure

1. Place the two tables or desks close enough together so that the 14-cm wooden rod can rest on both.

2. Tie one end of the string securely to a book. Tie the other end securely to the wooden rod. See Figure 1.

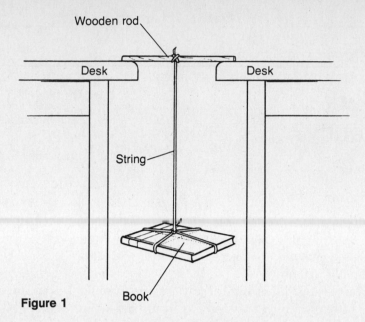

Figure 1

3. Rotate the wooden rod so that the string starts to wrap around it and the book begins to rise. Continue rotating the rod until you have raised the book as far as it can go. Determine how long it takes to do this. Record the time in the Data Table.
You may want to have students do this step one time as a trial run before they time themselves.

4. Lower the book to the floor. Tie the 7-cm rod to the other rod so that they are at right angles to each other. See Figure 2.

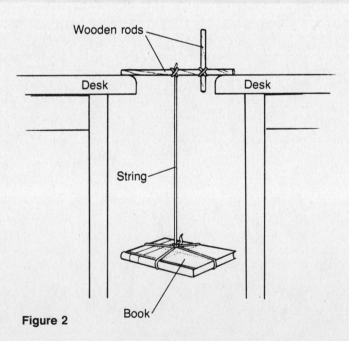

Figure 2

5. Use this shorter rod as a handle and rotate it to raise the book as before. Again determine how long it takes to do this and record the time in the Data Table.

6. Repeat steps 4 and 5 using the 14-cm rod and the 20-cm rod. Record your observations in the Data Table.

Observations

DATA TABLE

Book Raised by	Time (sec)	Relative Effort
Horizontal rod		
7-cm rod	Answers will vary but time and effort should decrease.	
14-cm rod		
20-cm rod		

Analysis and Conclusions

1. Is there an advantage to using the handle to raise the book? Explain.

Yes. It is easier with the handle.

2. Which handle made the work easiest? The 20-cm rod.

3. What simple machine is being used in this investigation? Wheel and axle.

Explain the role of each of the two rods in this simple machine.

Handle rod is wheel and horizontal rod is axle.

4. What is mechanical advantage? Amount by which a simple machine multiplies force.

5. What part of this simple machine determines its mechanical advantage?

The radius of the wheel.

Critical Thinking and Application

1. How did the use of a simple machine make you more efficient?

As the radius of the wheel increased, less effort and less time were required to do the work.

© Prentice-Hall, Inc.

2. Explain why with this simple machine work is made easier but does not increase.

A small force acts over a longer distance to produce a larger force acting over a shorter distance. A small

force times a longer distance equals a larger force times a shorter distance. Thus there is no increase in

work.

3. What law is followed by your answer to question 2?

Law of conservation of energy.

4. What other simple machine could be used to raise the book?

Pulley.

Going Further

Repeat this investigation using two books and four books. Determine the effect of increasing the resistance force on the mechanical advantage.

_____ *Laboratory Investigation* _____

The Inclined Plane

You may want to refer students to pages 380–381 in their textbook for a general discussion of simple machines and the inclined plane.

Time required: 35 minutes

Background Information

Any slope along which an object (a resistance force) is moved from a lower level to a higher level is considered an inclined plane. Stairs, ramps, and roadways that go uphill are examples of inclined planes.

Because there is usually a large amount of friction between the inclined plane and the object being moved, two kinds of mechanical advantage (MA) need to be considered: ideal mechanical advantage and actual mechanical advantage. Ideal mechanical advantage does not take friction into account and is calculated by dividing the length of the plane (the effort distance) by the height of the plane (the resistance distance).

Actual mechanical advantage takes the effort needed to overcome friction into account. It is calculated by dividing the resistance force by the effort force. Because friction cannot be completely eliminated, the actual mechanical advantage is always less than the ideal mechanical advantage.

In this investigation you will see how an inclined plane is used as a simple machine and how friction affects its mechanical advantage.

Problem

How is an inclined plane used as a simple machine?

Materials *(per group)*

wood board about 1 m long
   × 15 cm wide
spring balance
resistance (object such as book
   or small wood block)
string
meterstick
ring stand
clamp

Procedure

1. Using the spring balance, find the weight of the object and record it in the Data Table.

2. Measure the length of the wood board and record it in the Data Table. This length will be the same for all parts of this investigation.

3. Raise one end of the board 8 cm above the level of the ring stand and clamp it to the ring stand.

© Prentice-Hall, Inc.   **169**

4. Use the string to attach the spring scale to the object. Then use the spring scale to pull the object up the length of the board slowly and steadily. Note the force needed to do this and record it in the Data Table.

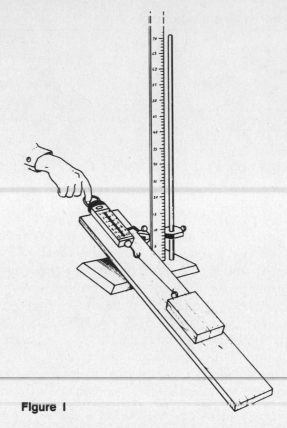

Figure 1

5. Raise the board 15, 30, and 40 cm above the level of the ring stand. Repeat step 4 for each height.

Observations

DATA TABLE

Height of Ramp	Length of Ramp	Resistance Force	Effort Force
8 cm	cm	N	N
15 cm	cm	Answers will vary. N	N
30 cm	cm	N	N
40 cm	cm	N	N

Analysis and Conclusions

1. Calculate the actual mechanical advantage (AMA) of the inclined plane when its height is

a. 8 cm _____   c. 30 cm _____

b. 15 cm _____   d. 40 cm _____

Answers will vary but should show an increase as the height increases.

170

2. Calculate the ideal mechanical advantage (IMA) of the inclined plane when its height is

    a. 8 cm _____   c. 30 cm _____

    b. 15 cm _____   d. 40 cm _____
    Answers will vary but should show a decrease as the height increases.

3. How does the actual mechanical advantage compare with the ideal mechanical advantage for each height of the inclined plane?

    The actual MA should be less.

Critical Thinking and Application

1. How do you account for the fact that the actual mechanical advantage and the ideal mechanical advantage are not the same? The actual mechanical advantage takes friction into account. Some extra effort must be used to overcome friction, and this lowers the AMA.

2. What general statement can be made about the height of an inclined plane and its actual and ideal mechanical advantage? Raising the height increases the AMA and decreases the IMA.

3. Explain your answer to question 2. As the board is raised, there is less friction, so the AMA increases. However, since the IMA = effort distance/resistance distance, raising the board increases the denominator and decreases the IMA.

4. What happens to the energy that is used to overcome friction?

    It is converted to heat.

© Prentice-Hall, Inc.

5. In a real machine, why is the work output always less than the work input?

Because some of the work input is used to overcome friction.

Going Further

1. Design an investigation to test various ways to reduce friction in an inclined plane. With your teacher's permission, perform the investigation.

2. Cut a piece of paper in the shape of a right triangle with a long hypotenuse. With a pencil or pen, shade the hypotenuse at the edge of the paper. Wrap the triangle around a pencil, making sure that the shaded edge is facing out so that it is visible. What simple machine does this resemble? Explain why a screw is considered to be a modified inclined plane.

Laboratory Investigation

Simple Machines—Levers

You may want to refer students to pages 383–386 in their textbook for a general discussion of simple machines and levers.

Time required: 40 minutes

Background Information

Simple machines make work easier to do. One way to express the benefit of using machines is called mechanical advantage (MA). The mechanical advantage of a machine is a number without units. If the mechanical advantage is more than 1, the machine makes work easier by multiplying the effort force. In other words, it causes an effort to seem larger than it actually is when acting against a resistance. If the mechanical advantage is less than 1, the machine makes work easier by allowing the resistance to move farther and faster than the effort. If the mechanical advantage is exactly 1, the machine makes work easier by changing the direction in which the effort must be applied.

A lever is a simple machine that involves two forces and a pivot point called a fulcrum. The force the user applies to the lever is called the effort or the effort force. The force against which the effort acts is called the resistance or the resistance force.

There are three classes of levers. The position of the two forces with respect to the fulcrum determines the class of the lever. In this investigation you will see how different positions of the effort, resistance, and fulcrum affect the mechanical advantage of the lever.

Problem

How does changing the positions of the effort, resistance, and fulcrum affect the mechanical advantage of a lever?

Materials (per group)

meterstick
spring balance
string
1-kg mass (or larger)
meterstick clamp or holder to
    serve as fulcrum

Procedure

1. Hang the mass from the spring balance to determine its force (weight) in newtons. Record this number in Observations as R.

2. Set up a first-class lever with the fulcrum at the 50-cm mark on the meterstick. Place the resistance (mass) and the effort (spring balance) at the distances indicated as resistance distance and effort distance, respectively, in A of Data Table 1. The effort force is the reading on the spring balance when the balance just balances the resistance. Calculate the mechanical advantage for this first-class lever. Record in Data Table 1.

3. Repeat step 2 three more times using the effort distances and resistance distances given for positions B, C, and D in Data Table 1.

© Prentice-Hall, Inc.

4. Set up a second-class lever with the fulcrum 10 cm from the end of the meterstick. Place the resistance (mass) and the effort (spring scale) at the distances indicated in A of Data Table 2. Apply the effort and record the effort force reading on the spring scale. Calculate the mechanical advantage for this second-class lever. Record in Data Table 2.

5. Repeat step 4 two more times using the distances given for positions B and C in Data Table 2.

6. For the third-class lever, do not use the meterstick clamp as the fulcrum. Place the end of the meterstick on the tabletop. This will be your fulcrum. Place the resistance (mass) and the effort (spring scale) at the distances indicated in A of Data Table 3. Apply the effort and record the effort force reading on the spring scale. Calculate the mechanical advantage for this third-class lever. Record in Data Table 3.

7. Repeat step 6 two more times using the distances given for positions B and C in Data Table 3.

Observations   Answers given are for a 1-kg mass. Answers will vary for other masses.

R = $\frac{9.8}{}$ N.

DATA TABLE 1   **First-Class Lever: Fulcrum at 50 cm**   Do not expect answers to be exact.

Position	Effort Distance	Resistance Distance	Effort Force	Mechanical Advantage $\left(\dfrac{R}{E}\right)$
A	40 cm	40 cm	10 N	1.0
B	40 cm	20 cm	5.0 N	2.0
C	40 cm	10 cm	2.5 N	4.0
D	20 cm	40 cm	20 N	0.5

DATA TABLE 2   **Second-Class Lever: Fulcrum at 10 cm from end of meterstick**

Position	Effort Distance	Resistance Distance	Effort Force	Mechanical Advantage $\left(\dfrac{R}{E}\right)$
A	50 cm	40 cm	7.8 N	1.25
B	50 cm	25 cm	5.0 N	2.0
C	50 cm	10 cm	2.0 N	5.0

DATA TABLE 3   **Third-Class Lever**

Position	Effort Distance	Resistance Distance	Effort Force	Mechanical Advantage $\left(\dfrac{R}{E}\right)$
A	20 cm	80 cm	>20 N	<0.5
B	40 cm	80 cm	20 N	0.5
C	60 cm	80 cm	12 N	0.8

Analysis and Conclusions

1. In the first-class lever, how did the effort force compare with the resistance force when the effort distance was equal to the resistance distance?

   They were about the same.

2. What was the mechanical advantage of the first-class lever in which the effort distance

   was equal to the resistance distance? Mechanical advantage = 1.

3. In the second-class lever, how does the effort force compare with the resistance force?

   The effort force is always less than the resistance force.

4. In the second-class lever, was the mechanical advantage the lowest when the resistance

   was close to the fulcrum or close to the effort? When the resistance was close to the effort.

5. In the second-class lever, was the mechanical advantage the greatest when the resistance was close to the fulcrum or close to the effort?

   When the resistance was close to the fulcrum.

6. Which third-class lever had the greatest mechanical advantage?

   The lever with the longest effort distance.

7. Which third-class lever had the least mechanical advantage?

   The lever with the shortest effort distance.

Critical Thinking and Application

1. In a first-class lever, where would you place the effort and resistance forces to have the

   greatest possible mechanical advantage? Resistance as close as possible to fulcrum; effort as far

   away as possible.

© Prentice-Hall, Inc.

2. In a second-class lever, how did moving the fulcrum closer to the resistance affect the amount of effort needed to balance the resistance? The closer the resistance was to the fulcrum, the smaller the effort force.

How did it affect the mechanical advantage? Moving the fulcrum closer increased the mechanical advantage.

3. If you wanted to have the greatest possible mechanical advantage for a third-class lever, would you move the effort closer to the fulcrum or closer to the resistance?
Closer to the resistance.

Explain. The longer the effort distance, the smaller the effort force necessary.

4. If the mechanical advantage of a third-class lever is always less than one, what is its benefit? A third-class lever causes the resistance force to move farther and faster than the effort force.

Going Further

Make a list of at least 15 items in your home that are levers. Indicate the class of lever to which each item belongs.

Laboratory Investigation

Chapter 15   Work, Power, and Simple Machines _____ **40** __

Pulleys As Simple Machines

You may want to refer students to pages 386–387 in their textbook for a general discussion of pulleys.

Time required: 45 minutes

Background Information

Pulleys are simple machines that are used in different ways to lift objects. The simplest kind of pulley is a grooved wheel around which a rope is pulled.

Pulleys can be used to change the direction of an applied force. For example, a pulley attached, or fixed, to the top of a flagpole allows you to raise the flag *up* by pulling *down*.

A combination of fixed and movable pulleys is called a pulley system, or block-and-tackle. A pulley system is used to multiply effort force in lifting heavy objects. Pulley systems are commonly seen around construction sites.

In this investigation you will see how different pulleys are used and determine the mechanical advantage of each.

Problem

How are pulleys used to raise objects? How is the mechanical advantage of a pulley or pulley system determined?

Materials (*per group*)

2 single pulleys	1 m nylon fishing line	spring balance
2 double tandem pulleys	ring stand and large ring	1-kg mass, or larger

Procedure

1. Find the resistance force of the mass you are using by attaching it directly to the spring balance. Record this resistance in the Data Table as the resistance for all of the pulley arrangements.

2. Set up a single fixed pulley as shown in Figure 1. Pull down on the spring balance to lift the mass. The reading on the balance shows the amount of effort needed to lift the resistance. Record this number in the Data Table.

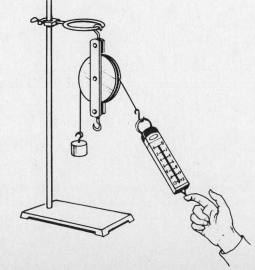

Figure 1

© Prentice-Hall, Inc.

3. Set up a single movable pulley as shown in Figure 2. Lift the mass by pulling up on the spring scale. The reading on the balance shows the amount of effort needed to lift the resistance. Record this number in the Data Table.

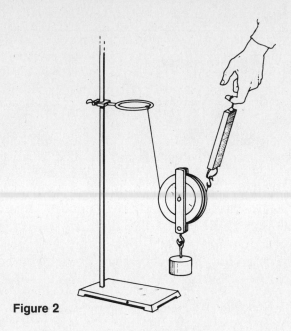

Figure 2

4. Set up the pulley system shown in Figures 3, 4, and 5. For each pulley system, measure the amount of force needed to lift the resistance and record it in the Data Table.

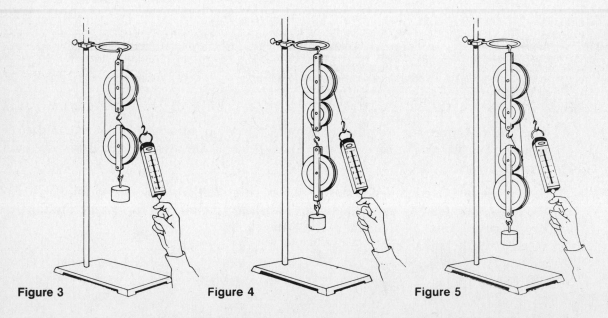

Figure 3   **Figure 4**   **Figure 5**

5. Calculate the mechanical advantage for each pulley and record these numbers in the Data Table.

Observations

DATA TABLE   The answers given here are sample data. The resistance of a 1-kg mass is approximately 10N.

Pulley Arrangements	Resistance (R)	Effort (E)	Mechanical Advantage (R ÷ E)
Single fixed	10N	10N	1
Single movable	10N	5N	2
Single fixed and single movable	10N	5N	2
Double fixed and single movable	10N	3.3N	3
Double fixed and double movable	10N	2.5N	4

Analysis and Conclusions

1. Was there a difference in the mechanical advantages you calculated for the single fixed

   pulley and the single movable pulley? <u>Yes.</u> Explain your answer.

   <u>The single fixed pulley has an MA of 1; the MA of the single movable pulley is 2.</u>

   _____

   _____

2. As you added pulleys to the system, what happened to the amount of effort force needed

   to raise the mass? <u>Less effort force was needed as more pulleys were added.</u>

   _____

   _____

3. How does the type of pulley or pulley system affect the mechanical advantage?

   <u>The number and arrangement of the pulleys determine what the mechanical advantage will be.</u>

   _____

   _____

Critical Thinking and Application

1. If a simple machine has a mechanical advantage of 1, effort force is not multiplied.

   Which type of pulley has a mechanical advantage of 1? <u>Single fixed pulley.</u>

   What is the practical use of this pulley? <u>It changes the direction in which the effort is applied.</u>

   _____

© Prentice-Hall, Inc.

2. To determine the mechanical advantage of a pulley or pulley system without arithmetic calculations, it is possible to simply count the number of sections of rope that support the resistance mass. The end section, to which the balance is attached, counts as a supporting section of rope *only when pulled up*. Using Figures 1 through 5, determine the number of supporting rope sections for each type of pulley.

    a. Figure 1 __1_____   d. Figure 4 __3_____

    b. Figure 2 __2_____   e. Figure 5 __4_____

    c. Figure 3 __2_____

3. Do the values obtained in question 2 agree with the calculated mechanical advantage in the Data Table? __Yes.__ Explain your answer. __Mechanical advantage for a pulley system is the__ __same no matter how it is calculated.__

4. Using two double pulleys, draw an arrangement of the pulleys that would give you a mechanical advantage of 5.   Student diagrams should show five supporting sections of rope.

5. When using any simple machine, you never "get something for nothing." Although the amount of effort force needed to lift a mass is reduced in a pulley system, something else is increased. What must be increased as the amount of effort force is decreased?

    The distance through which the effort moves is increased.

6. Explain your answer to question 5 in terms of work input and work output.

    In a machine, work output can never be greater than work input. Because work input is effort force ×

    effort distance, if the effort force is decreased, the effort distance must be increased.

Going Further

    Visit a construction site or an automobile repair shop that has a hoist to remove the engine from an automobile. Find out how pulley systems are used in these situations. Write a report of your findings.

_____ *Laboratory Investigation* _____

41

Investigating Factors Affecting a Pendulum

You may want to refer students to pages 404–406 in their textbook for a general discussion of the forms, conversions, and conservation of energy.

Time required: 30 minutes

Background Information

A pendulum demonstrates many of the laws of physical science. Several related factors affect the behavior of the pendulum. These factors include the length of the arc, the length of the pendulum, the mass, and the number of swings per minute. In this investigation you will study the behavior of a pendulum as several factors are changed.

Problem

How do various factors affect the behavior of a pendulum?

Materials *(per group)*

2-m length of cord
1-kg mass
support
0.5-kg mass

Procedure

1. Tie a cord at least 2 m in length to a support from the ceiling or doorway so that it can swing freely. Attach the 1-kg mass securely at the end of the cord. See Figure 1.

2. Start the mass swinging by releasing it from a measured height of 1 m above its lowest point, as shown in Figure 1. Remember to keep the cord taut. Count the number of swings in 10 sec and multiply by 6 to obtain the number of swings in 1 min. Record your answer in the Data Table. Repeat twice more and take an average for the number of swings in 1 minute.

© Prentice-Hall, Inc.

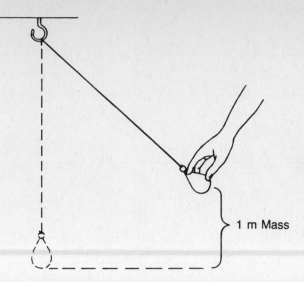

Figure 1

Point out to students that potential energy is converted to kinetic energy as the pendulum swings from the top of its arc, where it exhibits potential energy, through its full arc, where the falling pendulum exhibits kinetic energy.

3. Raise the pendulum to a height of 0.5 m above the lowest point. Release the mass, keeping the cord taut. Again, count the number of swings in 10 sec and multiply by 6 to obtain the number of swings in 1 min. Repeat twice more and take an average for the number of swings in 1 min. Record your answer in the Data Table.

4. Reduce the length of the cord by one half. Again, raise the mass 1 m over the lowest point, and keeping the cord taut, release the mass. Determine the average number of swings in 1 min, as you did in steps 2 and 3. Record your information in the Data Table.

5. Remove the 1-kg mass and replace it with a 0.5-kg mass. Raise the mass to a height of 1 m above its lowest point and, keeping the cord taut, release it. Determine the average number of swings in 1 min, as you did in steps 2, 3, and 4. Record your answer in the Data Table.

Observations

DATA TABLE

	Swings per Minute			
	Trial 1	Trial 2	Trial 3	Average
1-kg, full-length cord, 1 m high				
1-kg, full-length cord, 0.5 m high				
1-kg, half-length cord, 1 m high				
0.5-kg, full-length cord, 1 m high				
0.5-kg, full-length cord, 0.5 m high				
0.5-kg, half-length cord, 1 m high				

Analysis and Conclusions

1. By changing the height from which the mass is released in step 3, you change the length of the swing. How does the length of the swing affect the number of swings in 1 min?

It does not change the number of swings.

2. How does the mass of the pendulum affect the number of swings in 1 min?

It does not change the number of swings.

3. How does the length of the cord affect the number of swings in 1 min?

As the length of the cord decreases, the number of swings in 1 min increases.

Critical Thinking and Application

1. Examine a pendulum on a grandfather's clock or a cuckoo clock. How could you adjust the pendulum to speed up a slow clock?

Shorten the length of the string on the pendulum.

2. Based on what you know about free fall, why does the mass of a pendulum not affect the number of swings per minute? The force of gravity accelerates all objects at the same rate, regardless of their mass.

3. If the length of the swing does not affect the number of swings per minute, what must happen to the speed of the pendulum as the length of the swing is increased?

It must increase.

4. How would the motion of a pendulum be different if the pendulum were on the moon rather than on the Earth? Why? Because the force due to gravity is much less on the moon, the pendulum would accelerate more slowly and the number of swings per minute for a given length of string would decrease.

Going Further

The direction in which a freely swinging pendulum moves is not affected by the rotation of the Earth. Construct a pendulum that will swing a long while by using a heavy weight and a long cord. What does the apparent movement (after 15 min or so) of the line of swing of the pendulum tell you about the Earth?

Laboratory Investigation

Chapter 16   Energy: Forms and Changes

42

Investigating Energy and Falling Motion

You may want to refer students to pages 404–406 in their textbook for a general discussion of energy conversions.

Time required: 35 minutes

Background Information

When an object such as a ball falls, it accelerates and acquires kinetic energy, or energy of motion. If it does not reach terminal velocity, it acquires its maximum velocity and therefore its maximum kinetic energy just as it hits the ground. At that point, its motion is stopped and it is compressed. The kinetic energy is momentarily converted to potential energy, or stored energy. This potential energy is then converted back to kinetic energy as the ball bounces back. No ball will return to the exact height from which it was dropped because some of the kinetic energy is converted to other forms of energy, such as heat, when the ball strikes the ground. According to an important principle known as the law of conservation of energy, however, the total amount of energy does not change.

In this investigation you will describe the motion of a bouncing ball and examine how the ball demonstrates the law of conservation of energy. By plotting graphs, you will also examine how well different substances retain their original energy.

Problem

How can the motion of a bouncing ball be described and accounted for in terms of energy?

Materials (per group)

meterstick
tennis ball
Ping-Pong ball
sponge ball
air-filled rubber ball

Procedure

1. Have one member of your group hold the meterstick upright with the zero mark on the floor, as shown in Figure 1.

2. Have a second member of your group drop the tennis ball from the top of the meterstick (100-cm mark) in such a way that it does not touch the meterstick on the way down.

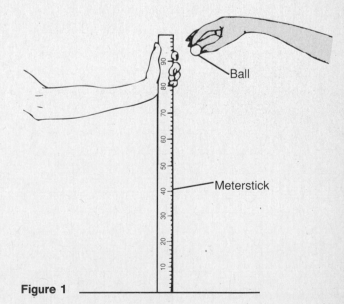

Figure 1

3. Have a third member of your group note the height of the first bounce. The bounce height should be called out to the fourth member of the group, who should record it in the Data Table. Let the ball continue to bounce and continue observing it for as long as you can. (It may take several trials because the ball may tend to bounce away from the meterstick.)

4. Repeat steps 1, 2, and 3 with the Ping-Pong ball, the sponge ball, and the air-filled rubber ball.

5. On Graphs 1 through 4, plot the height of each bounce for each ball. Draw a curved line that best fits through the vicinity of the points. You will plot four graphs.

Observations

DATA TABLE

Type of Ball	First Bounce	Second Bounce	Third Bounce	Fourth Bounce	Fifth Bounce	Sixth Bounce
Tennis						
Ping-Pong						
Sponge						
Air-filled rubber ball						

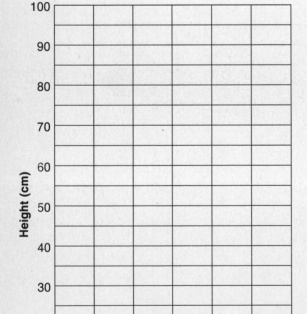

GRAPH 1 Tennis Ball

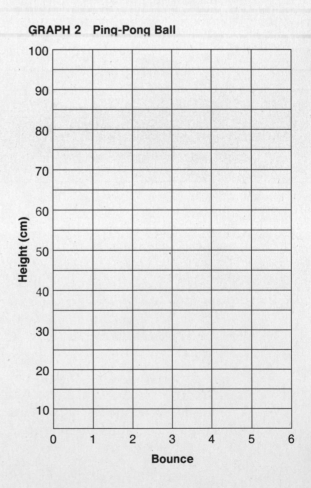

GRAPH 2 Ping-Pong Ball

GRAPH 3   Sponge Ball

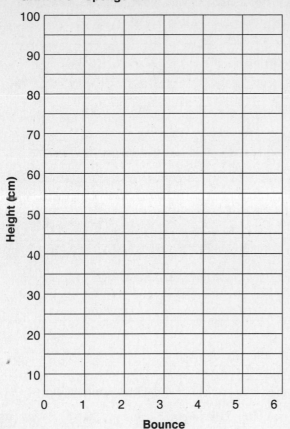

GRAPH 4   Rubber Ball

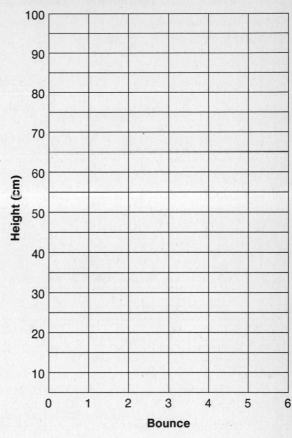

Analysis and Conclusions

1. Which ball retained the greatest percentage of its kinetic energy on each bounce?

   The Ping-Pong ball.

2. Explain the shape of each line on the graphs. Why were they similar?

   Each successive bounce was a fraction of the bounce before it, so the lines are curved.

3. What type of ball seems to bounce the least? Why?

   The sponge ball, because the material in the sponge ball absorbs the kinetic energy when it is

   compressed, and does not return as well to its original shape.

Critical Thinking and Application

1. Why can't a ball bounce higher than the height from which it is dropped?

   If it did so, ___ould have gained kinetic energy. This is not consistent with the law of conservation of energy.

2. Suppose you had carried out this investigation using a carpeted floor. How would your results have been affected? The height of the bounces would have been less, and the balls may have tended to bounce off at an angle rather than straight up.

3. Explain your answer to question 2. The carpet would absorb some of the kinetic energy of each ball, and the rough surface of the carpet would cause the balls to bounce back in an irregular way.

4. What do you think would happen to the kinetic energy if a Ping-Pong ball collided with a sponge ball? The sponge ball would probably bounce off the Ping-Pong ball in much the same way as it bounced off the floor. The Ping-Pong ball, however, would probably lose a considerable amount of kinetic energy by having it absorbed by the sponge ball.

Going Further

1. Sometimes it is necessary to develop materials that will absorb kinetic energy, such as car bumpers and padded dashboards. Try to develop a container that will keep an egg from breaking if dropped from a great height. Remember, try to surround the egg with materials that will absorb the energy of the impact and not permit that energy to be transferred to the egg.

2. Conduct an experiment with two balls of similar materials suspended by cords. Pull the balls apart and let them collide with each other. How many bounces do they undergo before stopping?

Laboratory Investigation

43

Investigating Heat Transfer

You may want to refer students to pages 426–429 in their textbook for a general discussion of heat transfer.

Time required: 40 minutes

Background

The movement of heat is called heat transfer. There are three types of heat transfer: conduction, convection, and radiation. In conduction, heat is transferred through a substance or from one substance to another by the direct contact of one molecule with another. In convection, molecules of liquids or gases move in currents, transferring heat as they move. In radiation, heat energy is transferred through space.

Heat energy sets molecules in motion. And temperature is a measurement of that motion. In this investigation you will transfer heat energy from a fuel to water, causing the water to boil. You will then use the boiling water to transfer heat to cold water.

Problem

How is heat transferred?

Materials _(per group)_

4 100-mL beakers
100-mL graduated cylinder
Bunsen burner
heat-resistant gloves
tripod

wire gauze
Celsius thermometer
glass-marking pencil
safety goggles

Procedure

1. Label the four beakers 1, 2, 3, and 4. Into Beaker 1 pour 100 mL of tap water. Measure the temperature of the water and record it in the Data Table.

2. Place the beaker on a tripod covered with gauze. Put on your safety goggles. Position the Bunsen burner beneath the beaker and light it. **CAUTION:** _Be careful whenever lighting and using an open flame._ Heat the beaker until the water is boiling.

3. While the water in Beaker 1 is coming to a boil, pour 25 mL of tap water into both Beaker 2 and Beaker 3. Record the temperature of each beaker in the Data Table.

4. When the water in Beaker 1 is boiling, record its temperature. Shut off the Bunsen burner. Wearing heat-resistant gloves, carefully pour the boiling water from Beaker 1 into Beaker 2. Immediately record the resulting temperature of the mixed water in Beaker 2 in the Data Table.

5. Pour 50 mL of tap water into Beaker 4 and repeat step 2. When the water in Beaker 4 is boiling, record its temperature and shut off the heat source. Wearing heat-resistant gloves, immediately—but carefully—pour the boiling water into Beaker 3. Record the temperature of the resulting mixture in the Data Table.

© Prentice-Hall, Inc.

Observations

DATA TABLE

Temperature of tap water in Beaker 1 _____ °C

Temperature of boiling water in Beaker 1 _____ °C

Temperature of tap water in Beaker 2 _____ °C

Temperature of tap water in Beaker 3 _____ °C

Temperature of water in Beaker 2
   after water in Beaker 1 has been added _____ °C

Temperature of boiling water in Beaker 4 _____ °C

Temperature of water in Beaker 3
   after water in Beaker 4 has been added _____ °C

1. What was the temperature of the water immediately after mixing the boiling water in Beaker 2? In Beaker 3?

Answers will vary.

2. What was the temperature change of the water in Beaker 2? In Beaker 3?

Answers will vary.

3. What was the temperature change of the boiling water in Beaker 1 when it was mixed

with the tap water? _____Answers will vary.____ In Beaker 4? _Answers will vary.____

Conclusions

1. Based on the temperature increases in Beakers 2 and 3, did Beaker 1 or Beaker 4 deliver

more heat? _Beaker 1_____

2. The water in Beakers 1 and 4 was at the same temperature while boiling but did not contain the same amount of energy. Since the amount of water was not the same in Beakers 1 and 4 but the temperature was the same, what do you think temperature is

actually measuring? _Temperature is a measurement of the average kinetic energy of molecules. Heat

is measured in units called calories. The number of calories (amount of heat) needed for a certain

temperature change depends on the mass of the substance being heated. Since Beaker 1 has a greater

mass of water than Beaker 4 and both beakers of water have been raised to the same temperature,

Beaker 1 must contain a greater amount of energy._

Critical Thinking and Application

1. When boiling water and tap water are mixed, how does the temperature of the mixture compare with the original temperatures of the water?

   The temperature of the mixture is between the two original temperatures.

2. Could the temperature of the mixture of boiling water and tap water ever reach the temperature of the boiling water? Explain.

   No, because the boiling water must give up some of its heat to the cooler water.

3. Suppose 100 mL of boiling water is mixed with 100 mL of tap water. How would the temperature of this mixture compare with the temperature of a mixture of 100 mL of boiling water and 25 mL of tap water? Explain your answer.

   The temperature of the first mixture would be lower because more tap water is present to absorb heat

   from the boiling water.

4. Design an experiment in which you could investigate the temperatures of mixtures resulting from various proportions of boiling water and tap water.

   Answers will vary.

Going Further

   Boiling water does not always have the same temperature. The boiling temperature depends in part on the air pressure above the water. Find out why pressure is so important for determining the boiling point.

© Prentice-Hall, Inc.

—————————— *Laboratory Investigation* ——————————

44

Heat of Combustion of a Candle

You may want to refer students to pages 435–439 in their textbook for a general discussion of measuring heat.

Time required: 40 minutes

Background Information

Combustion is the process during which oxygen in the air reacts with a substance to produce heat and light. In this investigation you will determine the amount of heat produced when a candle burns. A device that measures heat is called a calorimeter. Your calorimeter will be a can of water. You will measure the temperature change and the amount of water that is heated in the can. The product of the mass of water heated and its temperature change is equal to the amount of heat in calories released by the burning candle.

Problem

How many calories of heat are released per gram by a burning candle?

Materials *(per group)*

296-mL tin can, open at one end*
1.4-L tin can, open at both ends†
tin can lid‡
candle
stirring rod
ring stand and ring
100-mL graduated cylinder
Celsius thermometer
ice cube
matches
balance
metric ruler
safety goggles

*(10 oz) Use a soup can for the calorimeter. Punch two holes for the stirring rod about 1 cm from the can's top.
†(46 oz) Use a 1.4-L fruit juice can for the chimney. Punch out holes at the bottom with a hand can opener. Remove the jagged metal. Then remove the top and bottom of the can.
‡Use the top lid that you removed from the soup can.

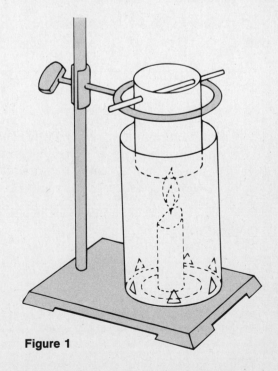

Figure 1

Procedure

1. Insert the glass stirring rod through the two holes in the small tin can. Hang the tin can by the stirring rod on a support ring as shown in Figure 1.

2. Attach the candle to the tin can lid with a few drops of melted wax. Place the candle under the hanging can. Measuring the distance with a ruler, adjust the can so it is 5 cm above the wick of the candle.

© Prentice-Hall, Inc.

3. Remove the tin can and stirring rod.

4. Record the mass of the candle and lid to the nearest 0.1 g. Enter this value in the Data Table.

5. Replace the candle on the ring stand and place the large can over the candle, with the air vents at the bottom. See Figure 1.

6. Fill the small can half full with tap water. Cool the water with ice until the temperature drops to 10 to 15°C below room temperature. Remove any excess ice. Record the temperature to the nearest 0.1°C in the Data Table.

7. Light the candle. Immediately replace the can of water on the iron ring. **CAUTION:** *Be extremely careful when lighting and working with an open flame.*

8. Move the thermometer through the water very gently and note the temperature.

9. When the water temperature is about the same number of degrees above room temperature as it was below when the ice was added, blow out the candle.

10. Keep moving the thermometer through the water and record in the Data Table the highest temperature the water reached.

11. Find the mass of the candle and lid again. Record the mass in the Data Table.

12. Use the graduated cylinder to measure the volume of the water in the can. If the amount of water is greater than 100 mL, measure the first 100 mL and then measure the remaining water. Add the measurements together and record the mass in the Data Table.

Observations

DATA TABLE

Mass of candle + base before burning		45.3 g
Lowest temperature		16.0 °C
Highest temperature	Sample	37.0 °C
Mass of candle + base after burning	data	44.2 g
Volume of water		320 mL

1. Calculate the change in temperature of water.   37.0°C − 16.0°C = 21.0°C

2. Calculate the amount of heat absorbed by the can of water. Heat in calories is the product of the mass of water and the change in temperature of the water. Since the density of water is nearly 1 g/mL, the mass of water is numerically equal to the volume of water. Therefore, the equation for heat is

Heat = Volume of water × Temperature change   320 mL × 21.0°C = 6720 cal

3. Calculate the mass of candle wax burned (Mass before burning − Mass after burning).
45.3 g − 44.2 g = 1.1 g

Conclusions

1. Calculate the heat released per gram of candle wax (heat absorbed by water divided by the mass of candle wax burned). $\frac{6720 \text{ cal}}{1.1 \text{ g}}$ = 6100 cal/g

2. Was all of the heat released by the candle absorbed by the water? Explain your answer.

No. A small amount of heat was absorbed by the metal of the calorimeter.

_____

_____

Critical Thinking and Application

1. A certain candle has a mass of 15 grams. How much heat will be released when the candle burns to one third its original height?   10 g × 6100 cal/g = 61,000 cal

2. How many grams of candle wax would be needed to heat 500 mL of water at 25°C to a temperature of 35°C?   Calories needed = 500 mL × 10°C = 5000 cal
5000 cal/6100 cal per gram = 0.82 g candle wax

3. A certain liquid X requires 0.5 calories per gram to have its temperature raised 1°C. Would 1 gram of candle wax produce enough heat to raise 1 kilogram of X 10°C?

Explain your answer. Yes, because less heat than 1 gram of candle wax produces (6100 cal) is

required for this change: 0.5 cal/g·°C × 1000 g × 10°C = 5000 cal.

_____

4. Based on this investigation, suggest a method for determining the calorie content of a

certain food. The calorie content of a food can be determined by using a setup much like the one used

in this investigation. The change in mass of the food, the change in temperature of the water, and the

volume of water involved must be determined in order to calculate the heat released by 1 gram of the

food.

Going Further

Repeat the procedure using a different-sized candle. Again calculate the heat required to burn 1 g of candle wax. Compare your answer with the answer obtained in the original procedure.

© Prentice-Hall, Inc.

_____ *Laboratory Investigation* _____

Chapter 17   What Is Heat? _____ **45** __

Specific Heat

You may want to refer students to pages 436–438 in their textbook for a general discussion of specific heat.

Time required: 45 minutes

Background Information

When heat is transferred from a warmer object to a cooler one, the law of conservation of energy predicts that the amount of heat gained by the cooler object will equal the amount of heat lost by the warmer object. But the temperature increase of one object will not necessarily equal the temperature decrease of the other object. This is because objects differ in their *specific heat*. Specific heat is a measurement of the number of calories of heat needed to raise the temperature of an object by a certain amount. More specifically, the specific heat of an object is the number of calories needed to raise the temperature of 1 gram of the object 1 degree Celsius. The higher the specific heat, the more heat it takes to raise an object's temperature. The lower the specific heat, the greater the temperature change with the addition of heat.

In this investigation, a hot metal mass will be placed in cool water in a calorimeter. Heat will be transferred from the hot metal to the water, and the specific heat of the metal will be calculated.

Problem

How can specific heat be determined?

Materials *(per group)*

Celsius thermometer
triple-beam balance
calorimeter   Two Styrofoam cups, one inside the other, and a cover with a slit for the thermometer make
hot plate   a suitable calorimeter.
250-mL beaker
3 pieces of string, each 15 cm
   long
safety goggles
3 metal disks with hole: The metal disks must be suspended by string in the beaker of water, so a hole
brass, lead, aluminum   in each disk is necessary.

Procedure

  1. Put on safety goggles. Half fill the beaker with water and heat it to boiling on the hot plate. Proceed with the next step while waiting for the water to boil.

2. Find the mass of the calorimeter cup. Half fill the cup with tap water and determine the mass of the cup plus water. Calculate the mass of the cool water by subtracting the mass of the cup from the mass of the cup plus water.

3. Record the temperature of the cool water in the calorimeter in the Data Table.

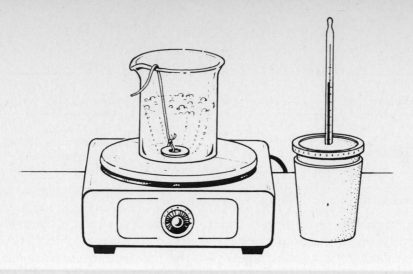

Figure 1

4. Measure the mass of one of the disks. Tie a piece of string around the disk and lower it into the boiling water so that the string hangs over the side of the beaker. Do not let the string touch the hot plate. Leave the metal disk in the boiling water for about 5 minutes to allow it to heat up to the same temperature as the water.

5. Measure and record the temperature of the boiling water. This will also be the temperature of the metal disk in the water.

6. Using the end of the string outside the beaker, remove the metal disk from the boiling water and *quickly* place it in the calorimeter cup. Cover the cup *immediately*. Note the thermometer reading. When the temperature stops rising, record this temperature as the final temperature of the water.

7. Calculate the change in temperature of the metal and the change in temperature of the cool water. Record these numbers in the Data Table.

Temperature change is the difference between the starting and final temperatures.

8. Repeat steps 2 through 7 for the remaining metal disks.

Observations

DATA TABLE

	Brass	Lead	Aluminum
Mass of calorimeter			
Mass of calorimeter and water			
Mass of water	Answers	will vary.	
Mass of metal			
Starting temperature of cool water			
Starting temperature of metal	100°C	100°C	100°C
Final temperature of water			
Final temperature of metal	Answers	will vary.	
Temperature change of water			
Temperature change of metal			

Conclusions

1. Calculate the heat gained by the cool water for each metal disk. Use the formula

$$\text{Heat gained by water} = \frac{\text{Mass of water} \times \text{Specific heat of water}}{\times \text{Change in temperature of water}}$$

The specific heat of water is 1 cal/g·°C

a. Cool water with brass __Answers will vary._____

b. Cool water with lead __Answers will vary._____

c. Cool water with aluminum __Answers will vary._____

2. Because the heat gained by the water in each case equals the heat lost by the metal, calculate the specific heat of each metal using the formula

$$\text{Heat lost by metal} = \frac{\text{Mass of metal} \times \text{Specific heat of metal}}{\times \text{Change in temperature of metal}}$$

a. Brass __For each metal, this number is the same as the answer to 1a, 1b, and 1c.__

Answers will vary, but they should be reasonably close to the

b. Lead __actual values given in Critical Thinking and Application 1.__

c. Aluminum _____

Critical Thinking and Application

1. The actual specific heats of the metals used in this investigation are brass, 0.09 cal/g·°C; lead, 0.03 cal/g·°C; aluminum, 0.22 cal/g·°C. How closely do the specific heats you calculated agree with these figures?

Answers should be reasonably close.

2. What three variables might have made your calculated results inaccurate?

The metal disks may not have been heated to 100°C. The Styrofoam cups may have allowed heat to

escape. When the metal disks were transferred to the calorimeter, some heat may have been lost.

3. Water has one of the highest specific heats of any common substance, 1.0 cal/g·°C. Explain how this fact is related to the fact that shore areas tend to be cooler than inland areas in the summer and warmer than inland areas in the winter.

Water must absorb a large quantity of heat before its temperature rises, so water remains cooler for a

longer time than land does in summer. In winter, the water cools off more slowly than the land, thus

retaining its heat for a longer time.

4. The specific heat of ethanol is 0.59 cal/g·°C. If you spilled boiling alcohol on yourself, would there be any difference in the severity of that burn compared with the burn caused

by boiling water? ____Yes____ Explain your answer.

Boiling alcohol does not contain as much heat as boiling water, so the burn would not be as severe.

_____

_____

Going Further

How would the results of this investigation be different if salt water or alcohol were used in place of tap water? State your hypothesis and design an investigation to determine if your hypothesis is correct. With your teacher's permission, perform the investigation and record your observations and conclusions.

Laboratory Investigation

46

Comparing Color and Radiation Absorption

You may want to refer students to pages 458–460 in their textbook for a general discussion of solar heating.

Time required: 40 minutes

Background Information

All hot objects, such as the sun, lighted lamps, and campfires, can transmit heat through space. This transmission can take place with or without the presence of molecules. Radiant heat energy is transmitted by the same mechanism as the transmission of radio waves and visible light. All such radiation is called electromagnetic radiation. The surface of the material being heated affects the degree to which radiant heat energy is absorbed by the material. Color is an important factor in heat absorption.

In this investigation you will use a thermometer to measure the amount of heat absorbed by different-colored surfaces and explain why one color does or does not absorb more heat than another. You will also graph and compare the change in temperature per unit time for the different surfaces. You will then be able to predict how shades of color on a surface affect the amount of heat absorbed.

Problem

What effect does color have on the ability of an object to absorb radiant heat energy?

Materials (per group)

100-W light source
2 coffee cans
heavy construction paper,
   1 white and 1 black sheet
corrugated cardboard, 12 cm ×
   12 cm
Celsius thermometer
classroom wall clock (with sweep
   second hand)
2 14-cm strips masking tape
2 different-colored pencils
scissors
ring stand and ring

Procedure

1. Cut the construction paper into rounds just larger than the opening of the coffee cans. Cover one of the coffee cans with the white paper circle and the other can with the black paper circle. Tape the edges with masking tape. See Figure 1.

© Prentice-Hall, Inc.

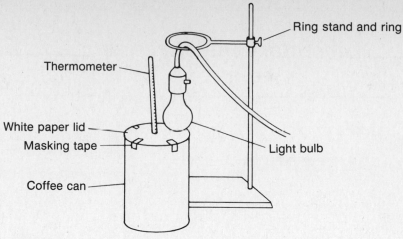

Figure 1

2. With a sharp pencil, carefully punch a hole in the centers of the construction-paper lids.

3. Carefully insert the thermometer bulb into the hole in the white lid.

4. Place this coffee can so that its lid is 5 cm beneath a 100-W lightbulb that is suspended by its wire from a ring stand and ring.

5. Switch on the lightbulb, which is a source of radiant energy. Record the temperature every 2 minutes for a period of 14 minutes in the Data Table. Switch off the light bulb after you have made the last observation.

6. Graph the data you have recorded for the white surface in colored pencil on the graph.

7. Carefully remove the thermometer from the white-lidded can and let the thermometer return to room temperature before starting with the black-lidded can.

8. Repeat steps 3 through 7 with the black-lidded can. Graph the data on the graph using a different-colored pencil.

Observations

DATA TABLE

White-Lidded Can		Black-Lidded Can	
Time (min)	Temp (°C)	Time (min)	Temp (°C)
0		0	
2		2	
4		4	
6		6	
8		8	
10		10	
12		12	
14		14	

GRAPH

The two graphs will curve upward toward the upper right. The curve for the black-lidded can will lie above that of the white-lidded can and will rise more steeply.

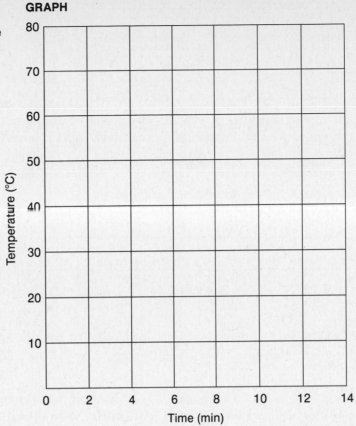

Conclusions

1. What effect does color have on the amount of radiant energy absorbed?

Dark colors absorb more radiant energy.

2. What effect does color have on the rate at which radiant energy is absorbed?

Dark colors absorb radiant energy faster.

Critical Thinking and Application

1. In warm, sunny weather, what color clothing should people wear to stay cool? Why?

Light colored. Light colors do not absorb the sun's radiant energy as rapidly.

_____

2. Design an experiment that could determine whether texture—in particular, shininess or dullness of surface—has any effect on the absorption of radiant energy. What effect would you expect? Several possibilities exist. Students could use mirrored materials and rough

materials. It is important to check that texture is the only variable. Shiny surfaces tend to absorb less

radiant energy than dull surfaces.

3. Many people have installed solar water-heating devices on the roofs of their houses. What color should these devices be in order to maximize their effect?

Black.

4. What happens to the light rays that are not absorbed by light-colored objects?

They are reflected.

5. Based on your answer to question 4, explain why a skier standing on a ski slope on a sunny day feels warmer than when standing on a black-topped pavement.

The sun's rays are reflected by the snow, causing the skier to feel warm. The black-topped pavement

absorbs the sun's rays, so they are not reflected onto the skier.

Going Further

1. List applications of the fact that color affects absorption of radiant energy. One example is the color of ice-cream vending trucks. See how many such examples you can observe in one day.

2. Conduct an experiment with two identical coffee cans and thermometers. Leave one empty (actually, full of air) and fill the other with water. Which heats faster? Which cools faster?

Laboratory Investigation

47

Constructing a Solar Furnace

This investigation must be done on a sunny day.

You may want to refer students to pages 458–460 in their textbook for a general discussion of solar heating systems.

Time required: 40 minutes

Background Information

As the cost of fossil fuels rises, many alternative sources of energy are being explored. One of these alternatives is solar energy. The sun is, directly or indirectly, the source of all energy on the Earth. The sun's energy can be directly used if harnessed properly. Many people have installed solar heating panels on the roofs of their houses. These devices are used to heat water for the people living in the building. Much research is being conducted in this area.

In order to maximize the energy from the sun, it is necessary to focus the sun's rays. Most often this is accomplished by using a curved mirrored surface, which reflects the rays back to a central point. Sometimes a magnifying lens accomplishes the same task by focusing the sun's rays to a point. A solar furnace is one example of this principle of focusing the sun's rays.

In this investigation you will construct a solar furnace with the capacity to boil water. A solar furnace is capable of developing high temperatures and should be treated with the same caution as a lighted Bunsen burner or an electric hot plate.

Problem

How does a solar furnace work?

Materials (per group)

automobile headlight reflector, with two holes punched in the rim
2 pieces of wood, about 3 cm wide, 1 cm thick, and 3 cm longer than the radius of the reflector (to be used as supports)
piece of wood, about 30 cm × 15 cm (for the base)
straight pins
cork large enough to fit snugly into the reflector hole
Pyrex test tube
wood screws

Before the lab period, use pliers to bend back the outer edge of the headlight reflector or have it done in your school's Industrial Arts department. A metal punch should be used to make two holes opposite each other in the bent rim. The holes should be large enough to accept the wood screws the students will use.

© Prentice-Hall, Inc.

Procedure

1. Insert a wood screw into each hole with a washer and attach the reflector to the wood supports as shown in Figure 1.

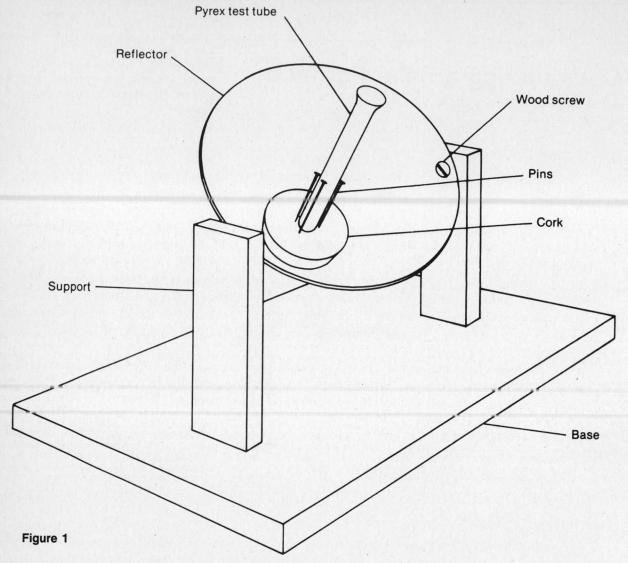

Pyrex test tube

Reflector

Wood screw

Pins

Cork

Support

Base

Figure 1

2. Attach the pieces of wood to the base with wood screws. At this point, check to be sure that the reflector can rotate easily on the wood screws. Tighten the screws just enough so that they can hold the reflector at any desired position.

3. Insert the cork into the hole intended for the bulb of the headlight. Make sure the cork fits tightly.

4. Insert the four pins into the cork in such a way that a test tube is held upright in the center of the reflector.

5. Aim the reflector toward the sun. All of the sun's rays should focus on the glass test tube.

6. When the reflector is in the proper position, stand behind the reflector and fill the test tube about one third full of water. Observe what happens.

Observations

1. In Drawing 1, trace the path of the sun's rays as they are reflected off the mirrored surface.

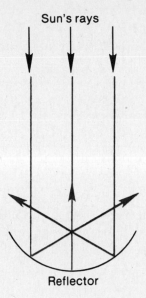

Sun's rays

Drawing 1   Reflector

2. What happens to the water in the test tube? How long does this take?

The water becomes hot and eventually comes to a boil. The amount of time depends upon the efficiency

of the particular apparatus.

Conclusions

1. Why does a reflector help the test tube get hot?

The rays become focused at a single point in the test tube.

2. Do you think the water would become hot without the reflector? Explain.

Yes, but probably not as hot and definitely not as quickly, because the sunlight hitting the tube would be

less intense.

Critical Thinking and Application

1. Explain how the solar furnace could be improved to create even higher temperatures.

Several methods are possible. A lens could focus the sun's rays prior to reaching the reflecting mirror. A

large mirror could be used to focus more of the sun's rays.

© Prentice-Hall, Inc.

2. Explain how your solar furnace could be used to change the sun's radiant energy into mechanical energy. Many answers are possible. One example is to have the sun's rays heat water to run a turbine or a steam engine.

3. Why should you protect yourself from the sun on ski slopes and beaches?
Both snow and sand reflect sunlight, so a ski slope or a beach has the same effect as being surrounded by many reflectors.

Going Further

With adult supervision, devise a solar furnace using a magnifying lens. Attempt to position the lens in such a way that a large amount of sunlight is focused in a small area. **CAUTION:** *High temperatures can develop.*

_____ *Laboratory Investigation* _____

Conductors and Insulators

You may want to refer students to pages 485–492 in their textbook for a general discussion of electrical conductors and insulators.

Time required: 40 minutes

Background Information

When electrons move from place to place, an electric current is created. Not all materials allow electrons to flow through them. Materials that allow electrons to flow freely are called conductors. Materials that do not allow electrons to flow freely are called insulators. In this investigation you will test some common materials and determine which are electrical conductors and which are insulators.

Problem

Which materials are conductors and which are insulators?

Materials *(per group)*

1.5-V dry cell
1.5-V lamp with sockets
3 connecting wires, 30 cm long
test materials: penny (copper);
    dime (silver); paper; wax;
    glass; aluminum foil; plastic;
    paper clip; wood; rubber; cloth;
    pencil lead (carbon)

Procedure

1. Set up a dry cell, lamp, and connecting wires as shown in Figure 1. Have your teacher check your setup before proceeding.   Check student setups before allowing students to continue with step 2.

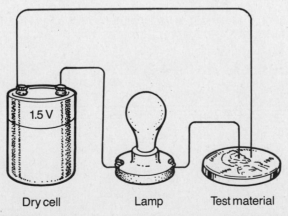

Dry cell   Lamp   Test material

Figure 1

© Prentice-Hall, Inc.

2. Keep the ends of the two test wires about 2 cm apart. Bring the ends of the wires into contact with each of the materials to be tested. Record your observations in the Data Table.

3. After you have tested all of the materials, disconnect the wires from the dry cell.

Observations

DATA TABLE

Material	Relative Brightness		
	Bright	Dim	No Light
Copper	✔		
Silver	✔		
Paper			✔
Wax			✔
Glass			✔
Aluminum foil	✔		
Plastic			✔
Paper clip	✔		
Wood			✔
Rubber			✔
Cloth			✔
Carbon		✔	

Analysis and Conclusions

1. Which of the materials you tested are good conductors of electricity? The coins, aluminum foil, and paper clip are good conductors. The carbon is a moderate conductor.

2. Which of the materials you tested are insulators? The paper, wax, glass, plastic, wood, rubber, and cloth are insulators.

Critical Thinking and Application

1. Are metals electrical conductors or insulators? <u>Conductors.</u>

2. Are nonmetals electrical conductors or insulators? <u>Insulators.</u>

3. Why is most electrical wiring, such as the connecting wires you used in this investigation, made of copper? <u>Because copper is one of the best conductors of electricity.</u>

Going Further

Strip about 8 cm of wood from one side of a pencil to expose the lead core inside the pencil. Hold the two ends of your test wires as far apart as possible and touch them to the lead core. Slowly move the wires closer together and observe what happens to the lamp. Use what you have learned in this investigation to explain your observations.

This is an example of variable resistance. Carbon is a moderate conductor of electricity. It resists the flow of electrons and is therefore a kind of resistor. As the copper wires are moved closer together, the resistance is overcome and the lamp gradually becomes brighter. This is the principle of the rheostat used to dim lights in the home.

© Prentice-Hall, Inc.

_____ *Laboratory Investigation* _____

Chapter 19   Electric Charges and Currents

49

Building Electric Circuits

You may want to refer students to pages 495–500 in their textbook for a general discussion of electric currents.

Time required: Part A—30 minutes
Part B—30 minutes

Background Information

An electric circuit allows the flow of electrons from a power source to make a complete round trip back to the power source. Most electric circuits contain several elements such as lights, transformers, and switches. In a series electric circuit, only one path is available for the electrons to flow through. In a parallel electric circuit, two or more paths are available for the electron flow. In this investigation you will construct series and parallel circuits and measure their current and voltage.

Problem

How are the current and voltage of an electric circuit determined?

Materials *(per group)*

3 1.5-V lamps with sockets
1.5-V dry cell
21 connecting wires
0 to 1-A ammeter
0 to 3-V voltmeter
knife switch

Procedure
Part A   A Parallel Circuit

1. Use the dry cell, connecting wires, and knife switch to connect the three lamps in parallel. See Figure 1. **Note:** *Be sure to connect the lamps to the dry cell and knife switch exactly as shown.* Make sure the knife switch is open. Post I must be connected to the positive terminal of the dry cell. Have your teacher check the circuit.
Check student setups before allowing students to continue with step 2.

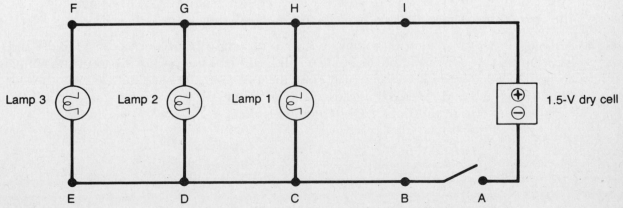

Figure 1

2. Close the knife switch and record your observation of the lamps.

All three lamps light equally brightly.

3. Unscrew the middle bulb. Record your observation.

The remaining lamps are still lit.

4. Retighten the middle bulb. Open the knife switch. Measure the total voltage of the circuit by placing the voltmeter as indicated in Figure 2. The positive terminal of the voltmeter must be connected to the positive post (I), and the negative terminal of the voltmeter must be connected to the negative post (B). Momentarily close the switch to see if the needle deflects to the right. If the needle deflects to the left, reverse the leads of the voltmeter. Record the total voltage (V_T) in the Data Table. Open the knife switch.

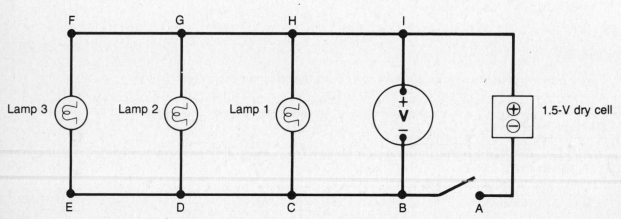

Figure 2

5. Measure the voltage across lamp 1 by connecting the positive lead of the voltmeter to post H and the negative lead to post C. Close the knife switch and record the voltage (V_1) in the Data Table. Open the switch.

6. Measure the voltage across lamp 2 by connecting the positive lead of the voltmeter to post G and the negative lead to post D. Close the switch and record the voltage (V_2) in the Data Table. Open the switch.

7. Measure the voltage across lamp 3 by connecting the positive lead of the voltmeter to post F and the negative lead to post E. Close the switch and record the voltage (V_3) in the Data Table. Open the switch and remove the voltmeter.

8. Measure the total current by removing the connecting wire between posts H and I and attaching the positive lead of the ammeter to post I and the negative lead of the ammeter to post H. See Figure 3. Momentarily close the switch. If the needle deflects to the left, open the switch and reverse the leads of the ammeter. Close the switch and record the total current (I_T) in the Data Table. Open the switch.

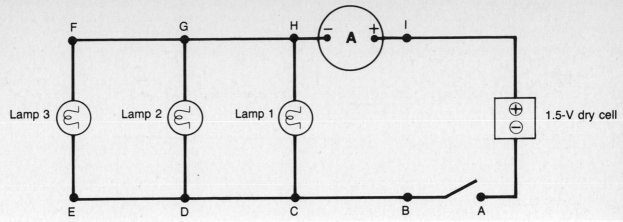

Figure 3

■ **9.** Disconnect the ammeter and replace the connecting wire between posts H and I. Disconnect the wire at post H that leads to lamp 1. Do not disconnect the wire at the lamp. Connect the negative lead of the ammeter to the wire that is connected to the lamp. Connect the positive lead of the ammeter to post H. See Figure 4. Close the switch and record the current (I_1) through lamp 1 in the Data Table. Open the switch, disconnect the ammeter, and reconnect the lamp wire to post H.

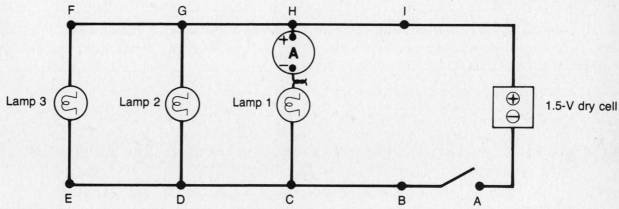

Figure 4

■ **10.** Disconnect the lamp wire from lamp 2 at post G. Do not disconnect it at the lamp. Connect the negative terminal of the ammeter to the lamp wire and the positive lead to post G. Close the switch and record the current (I_2) through lamp 2 in the Data Table. Open the switch, disconnect the ammeter, and reconnect the wire back to post G.

■ **11.** Disconnect the lamp wire from lamp 3 at post F. Do not disconnect it at the lamp. Connect the negative terminal of the ammeter to the lamp wire and the positive lead to post F. Close the switch and record the current (I_3) in the Data Table. Open the switch, disconnect the ammeter, and reconnect the lamp wire to post F.

© Prentice-Hall, Inc.

Part B A Series Circuit

⊪ 1. Connect the three lamps in series by removing the connecting wires between posts G and H, between E and D, and between C and B. Insert a connecting wire between posts E and B. Your circuit should now look like Figure 5. Have your teacher check your circuit. Close the switch and record your observation.

All three bulbs are dimly lit.

Check student setups before allowing students to continue with step 2.

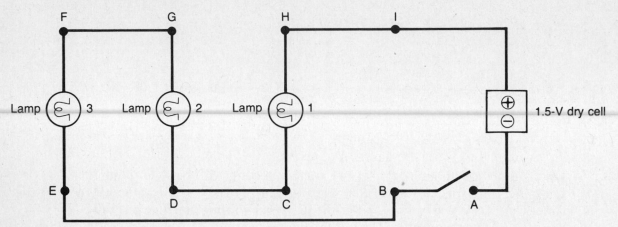

Figure 5

⊪ 2. Unscrew bulb 2 and record your observation. Tighten bulb 2 and open the switch.

No bulbs are lit.

⊪ 3. Connect the positive lead of the voltmeter to post I and the negative lead to post B. Close the switch. If the voltmeter deflects to the left, reverse the leads. Record the total voltage (V_T) in the Data Table. Open the switch.

⊪ 4. Connect the positive lead of the voltmeter to post H and the negative lead to post C. Close the switch and record the voltage (V_1) across lamp 1 in the Data Table. Open the switch.

⊪ 5. Connect the positive lead of the voltmeter to post D and the negative lead to post G. Close the switch and record the voltage (V_2). Open the switch.

⊪ 6. Connect the positive lead of the voltmeter to post F and the negative lead to post E. Close the switch and record the voltage (V_3) in the Data Table. Open the switch and remove the voltmeter.

⊪ 7. Measure the total current by removing the connecting wire between posts H and I and connecting the positive lead of the ammeter to post I and the negative lead of the ammeter to post H. Close the switch. If the needle deflects to the left, reverse the leads. Record the total current (I_T) in the Data Table. Open the switch, remove the ammeter, and replace the connecting wire between posts H and I.

⊪ 8. Disconnect the wire from lamp 1 at post C. Do not disconnect this wire at the lamp. Connect the positive lead of the ammeter to the lamp wire and the negative lead to post C. Close the switch and record the current (I_1) through lamp 1 in the Data Table. Open the switch, disconnect the ammeter, and reconnect the lamp wire to post C.

·❙❙⊨ **9.** Disconnect the wire from lamp 2 at post G. Do not disconnect it from the lamp. Connect the positive lead of the ammeter of the lamp wire and the negative lead to post G. Close the switch and record the current (I_2) in the Data Table. Open the switch, disconnect the ammeter, and reconnect the lamp wire to post G.

·❙❙⊨ **10.** Disconnect the wire from lamp 3 at post E. Connect the positive lead of the ammeter to the lamp wire and the negative lead to post E. Close the switch and record the current (I_3) in the Data Table. Open the switch, disconnect the ammeter, and reconnect the lamp wire to post E.

Observations

DATA TABLE

Circuit	Voltage (volts)				Current (amps)			
	V_T	V_1	V_2	V_3	I_T	I_1	I_2	I_3
Parallel	1.5	1.5	1.5	1.5	0.6	0.2	0.2	0.2
Series	1.5	0.5	0.5	0.5	0.1	0.1	0.1	0.1

Analysis and Conclusions

1. Add the currents I_1, I_2, and I_3 in the parallel circuit. Is the total current (I_T) approximately equal to the sum of the three individual currents in a parallel circuit?

0.2 A + 0.2 A + 0.2 A = 0.6 A = I_T

Yes; $I_T = I_1 + I_2 + I_3$

2. Add the voltages V_1, V_2, and V_3 in the parallel circuit. Is the total voltage equal to the sum of the individual voltages in a parallel circuit?

1.5 V + 1.5 V + 1.5 V = 4.5 V ≠ V_T No

3. In a parallel circuit, is the total voltage equal to the individual voltages?

1.5 V = V_T = V_1 = V_2 = V_3 Yes

4. Add the currents I_1, I_2, and I_3 in the series circuit. Does the total current equal the sum of the individual currents in a series circuit?

0.1 A + 0.1 A + 0.1 A = 0.3 A ≠ 0.1 A = I_T No

5. Is the total current approximately equal to the individual currents in a series circuit?

$I_T = 0.1 A = I_1 = I_2 = I_3$ Yes

6. Add the voltages V_1, V_2, and V_3 in the series circuit. Is the total voltage approximately equal to the sum of the individual voltages in a series circuit?

0.5 V + 0.5 V + 0.5 V = 1.5 V = V_T Yes

7. In which circuit would a burned-out bulb cause all the other bulbs to go out?

Series.

Critical Thinking and Application

1. Explain why all the bulbs in a series circuit go out when one bulb is disconnected.

In a series circuit, there is only one path for the electrons to take. When that path is disrupted, the current cannot flow.

2. Voltage is the force or "push" that gets electrons moving. Based on your data, explain why the bulbs in a series circuit burn dimmer than the bulbs in a parallel circuit.

In the series circuit, only 0.5 volt was available to push electrons through each lamp, but in the parallel circuit, 1.5 volts was available to push electrons through each lamp.

3. What would happen to the current in a parallel circuit if all the bulbs were not the same size? The current would divide unevenly, but the sum of the currents in each lamp would still equal the total current.

Going Further

Why are the lamps in a house lighting circuit not connected in series? Explain your answer.

Laboratory Investigation

50

Properties of Magnets and Magnetic Fields

You may want to refer students to pages 516–521 in their textbook for a general discussion of magnetism and magnetic fields.

Time required: 30 minutes

Background Information

Although magnets come in a variety of shapes and sizes, the simplest type of magnet is a straight bar made of iron. Like all magnets, a bar magnet has two ends, or poles: a north magnetic pole and a south magnetic pole. Magnetic forces are strongest at these poles. Surrounding the magnet is a magnetic field in which magnetic forces are also felt.

In this investigation you will use simple bar magnets and some iron filings to explore magnetism and magnetic fields.

Problem

What is a special property of magnets? How can you observe a magnetic field?

Materials (per group)

2 bar magnets
thread
2 pieces of wood, 10 cm long
index card
iron filings

Procedure
Part A   Properties of Magnets

1. Tie a piece of thread around the center of one bar magnet.

2. Hold the magnet by the thread so that the magnet can turn freely, as shown in Figure 1.

3. Bring the south pole of the other bar magnet near the south pole of the hanging magnet. Observe what happens.

4. Now bring the north pole of the magnet near the south pole of the hanging magnet. Observe what happens.

Figure 1

© Prentice-Hall, Inc.

Part B   Observing a Magnetic Field

1. Place a bar magnet between the two pieces of wood.

2. Cover the magnet with an index card. See Figure 2.

3. Sprinkle iron filings on top of the card. Gently tap the card several times to distribute the iron filings evenly. Observe what happens.

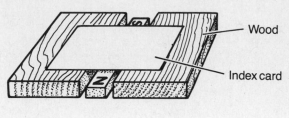

— Wood

— Index card

Figure 2

Observations

1. What happened when you brought the south pole of a bar magnet near the south pole of the hanging magnet?

   The two poles pushed away, or repelled each other.

2. What happened when you brought the north pole of the bar magnet near the south pole of the hanging magnet?

   The two poles pulled together, or attracted each other.

3. What happened when you sprinkled iron filings on the card over the bar magnet? The iron

   filings lined up with the magnetic field of the bar magnet, making it visible.

Analysis and Conclusions

1. What is a special property of magnets by which they can be identified? Magnets have unlike

   poles. They can attract and repel each other.

2. What is the shape of the magnetic field around a bar magnet, as shown by the pattern of

   iron filings? The magnetic field surrounds the magnet from pole to pole.

3. Where is the magnetic field strongest? At the poles.

   How can you tell? Most of the iron filings cluster at the poles.

Critical Thinking and Application

1. What rule describes the behavior of magnetic poles? <u>Like poles repel each other and unlike poles</u>

   <u>attract each other.</u>

2. How could you make the hanging bar magnet rotate without touching the magnet? <u>Hold a</u>

   <u>second bar magnet near the hanging magnet so that the opposite poles are near each other. Slowly</u>

   <u>make a circle with the magnet you are holding. It will pull the hanging magnet because of the attraction</u>

   <u>between unlike poles and cause it to rotate.</u>

   _____

3. Why does the magnetic field around a bar magnet form an arc between the north and

   south poles of the magnet? <u>Because of the force of attraction between the north pole and the south</u>

   <u>pole.</u>

   _____

Going Further

   Repeat Parts A and B of this investigation using magnets of different shapes and sizes. To make a permanent record of the magnetic field in Part B, use light-sensitive paper in place of the index card.

_____ *Laboratory Investigation* _____

Studying Electromagnetic Induction

You may want to refer students to pages 542–550 in their textbook for a general discussion of electromagnetic induction.

Time required: 40 minutes

Background Information

In 1831, Michael Faraday discovered that when a coil of wire is moved in a magnetic field, an electric current is generated, or induced, in the wire. This process is called electromagnetic induction. Electromagnetic induction involves cutting across magnetic lines of force.

In this investigation you will use a bar magnet and a magnetic compass with a coil of wire wrapped around it to detect an electric current in the wire. When an electric current flows through the coil of wire, the compass needle will move.

Problem

How can you create an electric current by moving a coil of wire in a magnetic field?

Materials *(per group)*

compass
bar magnet
connecting wire, 4 m

Procedure

1. Using a piece of wire 1 m long, wrap 20 loops of wire around the compass, as shown in Figure 1.

2. Place the compass on a table or other flat surface. Align the compass needle with the wire.

3. With the remaining 3-m length of wire, wind 10 loops of wire around your finger. The coil should be large enough for the bar magnet to fit through.

4. Connect the two coils of wire by twisting the ends of the wires together. The second coil should be at least 1 m away from the compass.

5. Slowly push the north pole of the bar magnet into the coil of wire. Observe what happens to the compass needle.

6. Remove the magnet and add 10 more loops of wire to the coil. Repeat step 5.

7. Slowly push the south pole of the magnet into the coil of wire. Observe what happens to the compass needle.

© Prentice-Hall, Inc.

8. Observe what happens to the compass needle as you slowly pull the magnet out of the coil of wire.

9. Repeat step 5, but this time push the magnet into the coil quickly.

Compass

Bar magnet

Figure 1

Observations

1. What happened when you slowly pushed the north pole of the bar magnet into the coil of wire? The compass needle was deflected. _____

   _____

2. What happened to the compass needle after you added 10 more loops of wire to the coil and pushed the north pole of the magnet into the coil? The compass needle was deflected _____

   further.

3. What happened when you pushed the south pole of the magnet into the coil of wire? The compass needle was deflected in the opposite direction. _____

4. What happened when you pushed the magnet into the coil quickly? The compass needle was deflected further.

Analysis and Conclusions

1. Explain what you observed happening when you moved a magnet in a coil of wire. When the magnet was moved into or out of the coil of wire, the wire cut across magnetic lines of force surrounding the magnet. This caused an electric current to be induced in the wire, as shown by the deflection of the compass needle. _____

   _____

2. What is this process called? Electromagnetic induction. _____

Critical Thinking and Application

1. How does the number of loops of wire affect the current in the wire? The more loops of wire,

the greater the current in the wire.

2. How did changing the pole of the magnet affect the direction of the current in the wire?

How can you tell? Changing the pole of the magnet reversed the direction of the current. The

compass needle was deflected in the opposite direction.

3. Would a current be induced in the wire if you did not move the magnet? Why or why

not? No, because the magnetic lines of force would not be cut if there was no motion.

4. Would a current be induced if you moved the coil of wire instead of the magnet? Why or

why not? Yes, because the magnetic lines of force are cut if either the magnet or the wire is moved.

Going Further

What do you think would happen if you made a coil of wire by turning 10 loops of wire in one direction and 10 loops in the opposite direction? Try it and find out.

Laboratory Investigation

52

Constructing a Telephone

You may want to refer students to pages 565–569 in their textbook for a general discussion of telephone technology.

Time required: 25 minutes

Background Information

The operation of the telephone involves energy conversions. In the transmitter of the telephone, sound waves are converted into electric waves that travel over wires. In the receiver of the telephone, electric waves are converted back into sound waves.

The first telephone conversation took place on March 10, 1876 between the inventor of the telephone, Alexander Graham Bell, and his assistant, Thomas Watson.

In this investigation you will build a simple device that illustrates the operation of a telephone transmitter.

Problem

How do carbon grains in the transmitter of a telephone affect the flow of electricity?

Materials *(per group)*

plastic cup	2 alligator clips
1.5-V lamp with sockets	1.5-V dry cell
carbon grains	3 connecting wires,
2 copper strips	30 cm long

Procedure

1. Place the two copper strips in either side of the plastic cup.

2. Half fill the cup with carbon grains.

3. Using an alligator clip, connect one end of a wire to one of the copper strips. Connect the other end of the wire to one side of the lamp socket.

4. Connect another wire to the other side of the lamp socket. Connect the other end of this wire to one of the dry cell poles.

5. Using an alligator clip, connect a third wire to the other copper strip. Connect the other end of the wire to the other dry cell pole. See Figure 1.

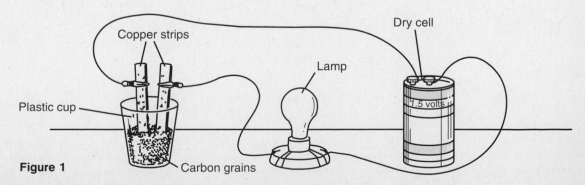

Figure 1

6. Squeeze the copper strips together, then let them go.

© Prentice-Hall, Inc.

Observations

1. What happens when you squeeze the copper strips together?

   The light bulb gets brighter.

2. What happens when you stop squeezing the copper strips together?

   The light bulb dims.

Analysis and Conclusions

1. How does pressure on the carbon grains affect the flow of electricity?

   The more pressure on the carbon grains, the stronger the electric current.

2. How does this investigation illustrate the operation of a telephone transmitter?

   In a telephone transmitter, sound waves strike the thin metal disk called the diaphragm. The diaphragm vibrates and presses against the carbon grains that conduct electricity. The greater the pressure on the grains, the stronger the electric current.

Critical Thinking and Application

1. How is the pressure on the carbon grains in a telephone transmitter regulated?

   By the loudness or softness of the speaker's voice.

2. How is the operation of a telegraph similar to that of a telephone?

   Electric signals are transmitted over wires.

   How is it different? In a telegraph, the circuit is either open or closed. There is no variation in the amount of current.

Going Further

Find out what new technology is being used in telephone communication.

Laboratory Investigation

Chapter 22   Electronics and Computers _____ **53** ____

Constructing a Simple Computer Circuit

You may want to refer students to pages 572–577 in their textbook for a general discussion of computers.

Time required: 40 minutes

Background Information

Computers use combinations of off-on (flip-flop) circuits to perform their various functions. A circuit that is on represents the number 1. A circuit that is off represents 0. The binary number system (base 2) has only two numbers—1 and 0. The computer uses the binary system to represent all numbers, letters, and commands. In this investigation you will construct an electric circuit that will convert decimal (base 10) numbers into binary (base 2) numbers.

Problem

How does an off-on computer circuit work?

Materials *(per group)*

3 1.5-V lamps with sockets
1.5-V dry cell
3 knife switches, single pole-single
   throw
knife switch, double pole-single
   throw
connecting wires
pegboard
machine screws
12 clips or screws for connecting
   wires

If the ends of the connecting wires are tinned with a little solder, the leads will last indefinitely. The posts can be just wood screws, but double-spring Fahnestock-type posts are much easier to use (Welch #S31067-15 or Fisher #S44358). The posts, lamps, and knife switch should be mounted on a piece of pegboard.

Procedure

1. Connect the lamps, switches, and dry cell on the pegboard as shown in Figure 1. Note that switch 3 must have two separate poles so it can be connected to both lamps 1 and 2.

2. Have your teacher check your circuit before you proceed.
   Check student circuits before allowing students to continue with step 3.

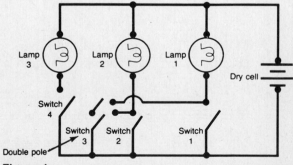

Figure 1

3. Switches 1, 2, 3, and 4 correspond to the decimal numbers 1, 2, 3, and 4. Close switch 1 and record which lamps are lit and which remain off. Record a 1 if lit, 0 if off. For example, if only the middle lamp is lit, record 010.

4. Open switch 1.

5. Repeat steps 3 and 4 for switch 2, then switch 3, and finally switch 4. Record each result in the Data Table.

Observations

DATA TABLE

Decimal	Binary
1	001
2	010
3	011
4	100

Analysis and Conclusions

1. Your circuit converted decimal (base 10) numbers to binary (base 2) numbers. Do your results in the Data Table agree with the following decimal-binary conversion chart?

Decimal	Binary
1	001
2	010
3	011
4	100
5	101
6	110
7	111

Student answers should agree with the conversion chart.

2. Only the first four decimal numbers were converted to binary numbers. Explain how you could convert the following decimal numbers to binary numbers using your circuit.

a. 5   b. 6   c. 7

If time permits, try these numbers on your circuit.

a. Close switches 4 and 1.   b. Close switches 4 and 2.   c. Close switches 4 and 3 or close switches 4,

2, and 1.

Critical Thinking and Application

1. What is the largest decimal number your circuit can convert? Why?

   The number 7, because 111 requires all the lamps to be lit.

2. What would you have to do to your circuit to go beyond this number?

   Add more lamps and switches.

3. What is the product of binary numbers 101 × 010? Write your answer in binary

   numbers. 1010 (ten)

4. What is the value of binary number 111101?

   61

Going Further

Each lamp corresponds to a bit on a computer. Each number or letter on a keyboard is represented as a byte. Find out how many bits make a byte. How many lamps would be required to represent a byte in your circuit?   8, 8

Laboratory Investigation

54

Creating a Computer Program

You may want to refer students to pages 572–577 in their textbook for a general discussion of computers.

Time required: 30 minutes

Background Information

The use of computers is becoming more and more evident in our daily life. They are extremely helpful in performing very complex tasks at great speed. In order for any computer to be used efficiently, it must be properly programmed. A program is a series of instructions placed in the computer's memory. These instructions order the computer to perform tasks and to make simple yes or no decisions.

Computer program designers must be able to think clearly and analyze the task to be done. They must be able to break down a complex task into simple ones. These simple tasks must be sequenced in the correct order. New information must be processed at just the right time.

In order to help analyze any task, program designers create flowcharts to describe and sequence the parts of a task. Various shaped boxes are used in a flowchart as symbols for different functions. See Figure 1.

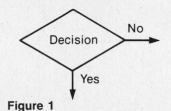

Start or Stop box describes the beginning or end of a program.

Input or Output box describes a step to input information or to write out some information.

Computation or Assignment box describes a computation to be carried out or assigns a new value to some item in the program.

Decision box describes a yes or no decision. Program makes decision on the basis of the answer.

Figure 1

In this investigation you will learn how to change a computer task into a flowchart using the flowchart symbols given.

Problem

How are computers programmed?

© Prentice-Hall, Inc.

Materials *(per student)*

paper
pencil

Procedure

1. Study the task indicated by the following question: "Is the combined age of the males in a certain family greater than the combined age of the females?"

2. Study the flowchart example in Figure 2, which shows you how to solve this task.

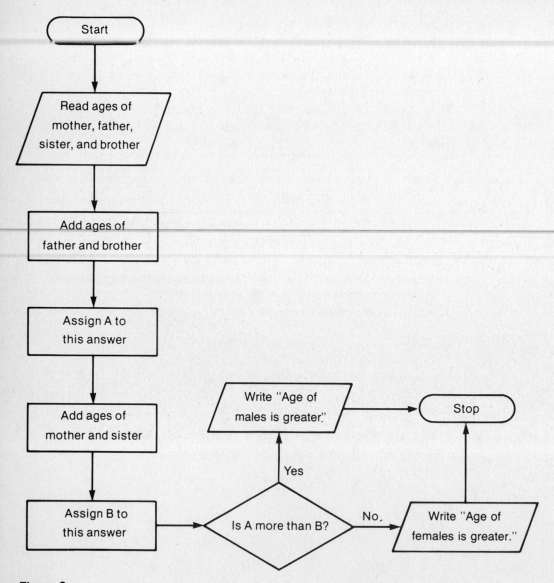

Figure 2

234

3. Write flowcharts in the space provided for Drawings 1 and 2 for the following questions. Use the symbols you have learned and the example shown in Figure 2.

　　a. Is the average of three test grades a passing mark (65 is passing)?
　　b. What is the cost of X kilograms of potatoes at Y cents per kilogram, and can a man with Z cents afford to buy them?

Observations

1. For question 3a, what information must be inputed? Test grades. _____

　_____

2. What decision must the computer make in question 3a?

　Whether the average of the three test grades is greater than or equal to 65, or less than 65. ___

　_____

　_____

　_____

3. How many different pieces of information must be inputed in question 3b? What are

　they? Three. The number of kilograms of potatoes, the cost per kilogram, and the number of cents the

　man has. _____

　_____

　_____

　_____

© Prentice-Hall, Inc.

Analysis and Conclusions

Drawing 1

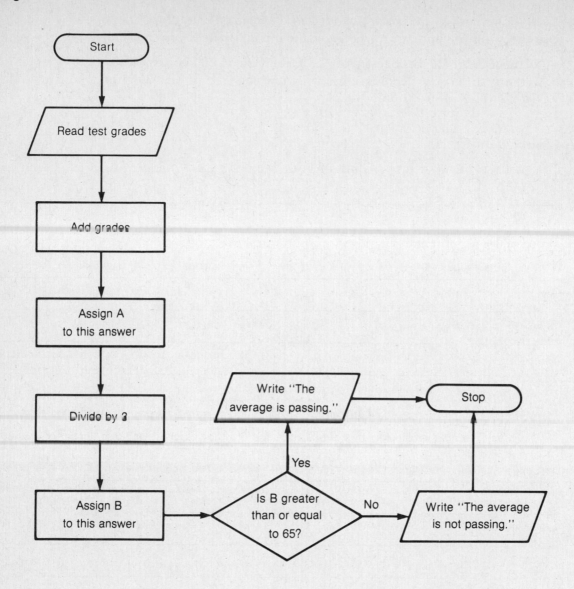

Drawing 2

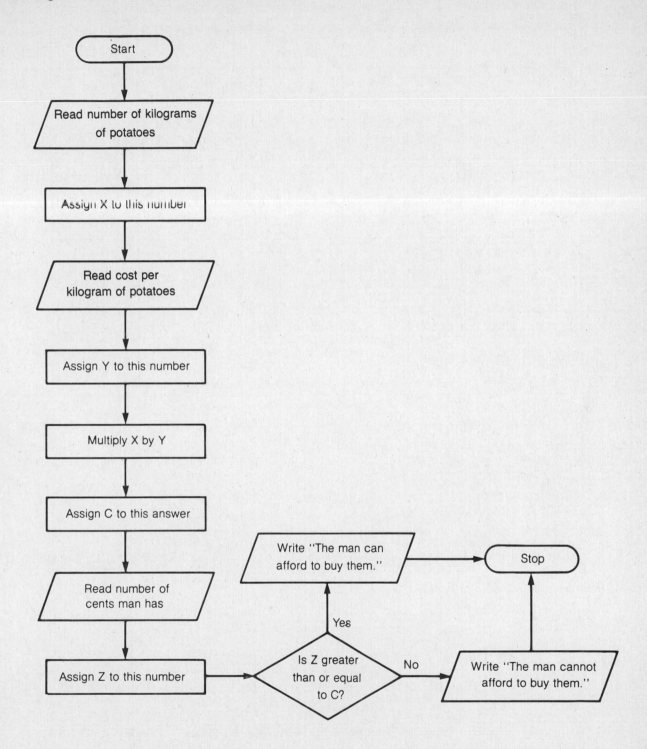

Critical Thinking and Application

1. Study the flowchart you made in Drawing 2. What would happen to your program if the first assignment box were left out? The computer would not "take" the number of kilograms of potatoes, and it would be unable to carry out the rest of the calculations involving X.

2. In Drawing 2, what would happen to your program if you forgot to multiply X by Y? The computer would think that C was equal to the cost per kilogram of potatoes, not the total price. Thus C would probably be too low, and the man would think he could afford what he could not.

3. A student running a program based on Drawing 1 finds that nearly every combination of test grades comes out passing, unless the sum of the grades is less than 65. What is probably wrong with the program? The student probably forgot to tell the computer to divide the sum of the grades by 3. Thus the computer is deciding whether the sum, not the average, is less than 65.

4. A student wants to see if a man with $1.50 can buy 2 kg of potatoes at 75 cents per kilogram. The student runs the program and finds that the man cannot afford the potatoes. What might the student have done wrong? The student either reversed the instructions in the decision box or inputed 1.5 for the number of cents the man has instead of 150.

Going Further

1. Learn how the binary number system can be used by a computer to make rapid electrical calculations.

2. Devise a flowchart for a program to play tic-tac-toe so that the computer never loses.

_____ *Laboratory Investigation* _____

Chapter 23   Characteristics of Waves

55

Waves and Wave Motions

You may want to refer students to pages 600–606 in their textbook for a general discussion of wave interactions.

Time required: 35 minutes

Background Information

Although all waves are not the same, they have many characteristics in common. Sound waves, light waves, water waves, and other types of waves are similar in both properties and behavior.

In this investigation you will study the behavior of water waves in a ripple tank. Your observations of the water waves will also apply to other types of waves.

Problem

What are the properties of moving waves?

Materials *(per group)*   This investigation may be done as a teacher demonstration on an overhead projector.

ripple tank   If ripple tanks are not available for student use, a large Pyrex baking dish supported between
light source two desks is a good substitute.
wood blocks
glass square (1.2 cm thick)
30-cm ruler
rubber hose or bendable metal
   strip to fit tank
large sheets of white paper
medicine dropper

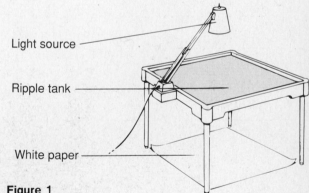

Light source

Ripple tank

White paper

Figure 1

Procedure

1. Set up the ripple tank as indicated in Figure 1.

2. Add water to a depth of 1.5 cm.
   As you perform steps 3 through 10, draw a diagram of what you see in each step in the space provided in Observations. Label your diagram according to the directions below:
   The crest of a wave should be drawn as a line.
   The direction in which the waves move should be shown by an arrow.
   The point of origin of the wave should be marked with an o.
   Any barrier that stops the wave should be marked with a b.

3. Place the ruler on its side in the tank and slowly move it back and forth a distance of about 1 cm. Draw the wave pattern and write a brief description of it under your diagram.

4. Repeat step 3 but move the ruler back and forth more rapidly. Draw the wave pattern and write a brief description.

© Prentice-Hall, Inc.

5. Place the wood blocks in the tank so that they form a barrier at an angle to the side of the tank. Slowly move the ruler back and forth as in step 3. Note the angle at which the waves bounce off, or are reflected from, the barrier. Draw the wave pattern and write a brief description.

6. Place the section of hose or metal strip in the ripple tank so that it forms a curved barrier. Move the ruler back and forth in the tank as in step 3. Draw the wave pattern both going toward the curved surface and reflected from it. Write a brief description.

7. Remove all objects from the ripple tank. When the water is still, use the medicine dropper to slowly let water droplets fall into the center of the ripple tank. Draw the wave pattern and write a brief description of it.

8. Use the wood blocks to form a barrier at an angle to one of the sides of the tank. Repeat step 7. Draw and describe the wave pattern.

9. Place the curved hose or metal strip in the tank as in step 6. When the water is still, let water droplets fall into the center of the tank as in step 7. Draw and describe the wave pattern.

10. Place the glass square in the pan near one side of the tank so that the sides of the square are parallel to the sides of the tank. Slowly move the ruler back and forth. Draw and describe the wave pattern.

Observations

Step 3

Step 4

Step 5

Step 6

Step 7

Step 8

Step 9

Step 10

Analysis and Conclusions

1. What type of waves were generated by the back-and-forth motion of the ruler?

   Longitudinal waves.

2. What type of waves were generated by the drops falling into the ripple tank?

   Transverse waves.

3. How did the waves generated in steps 3 and 4 differ from each other?

   The waves in step 4 had a higher frequency and a shorter wavelength.

4. What is the relationship between the frequency and wavelength of a wave?

   The higher the frequency, the shorter the wavelength, and vice versa.

5. In step 5, how did the angle at which the waves hit the barrier compare with the angle at
   which they were reflected? They were reflected at the same angle at which they hit.

6. How did the waves reflected from the straight surface differ from the waves reflected
   from the curved surface? All the waves reflected from the curved surface came together at a single
   point.

7. How is the behavior of the waves generated by the water drop different from that of the
   waves generated by the ruler? The waves generated by the water drop formed a circular pattern.
   This is the only difference.

© Prentice-Hall, Inc.

Critical Thinking and Application

1. Do the waves generated by the movement of the ruler represent longitudinal waves or transverse waves? <u>Longitudinal waves.</u> Explain. <u>The back-and-forth movement of the ruler generates</u> <u>this type of compression wave.</u>

   _____

2. Do the waves generated by the falling droplets of water represent longitudinal waves or transverse waves? <u>Transverse waves.</u> Explain. <u>When the drop falls, it causes a vertical disturbance</u> <u>in the water, resulting in a transverse wave.</u>

   _____

3. Were there any differences in the behavior of the waves formed by the moving ruler and those formed by the droplets of water? <u>No.</u> Explain. <u>All types of waves behave</u> <u>similarly.</u>

   _____

4. Review the diagrams you drew as part of your observations. In which diagram(s) did you observe the following wave interactions?

   a. Reflection <u>5, 6, 8, 9 (and to a lesser degree 3 and 4)</u>

   b. Refraction <u>10</u>

   c. Diffraction <u>5, 8</u>

   d. Interference <u>6, 9</u>

Going Further

Repeat the above investigation generating waves from two sources (rulers or droppers) at the same time. Draw and describe the wave patterns formed. How do these wave patterns differ from the wave patterns formed in this investigation?

Laboratory Investigation

Chapter 24   Sound and Its Uses

56

Determining the Speed of Sound

You may want to refer students to pages 614–618 in their textbook for a general discussion of the speed and transmission of sound.

Time required: 45 minutes

Background Information

Sound travels at different speeds through different materials. This is because some materials transmit sound better than others. Liquids transmit sound much faster than gases do. For example, sound travels about four and one half times faster through water than through air. If you have ever been swimming in a pool, you may have noticed that sound is transmitted faster under water. Many solids are even better sound transmitters. Temperature also affects how rapidly sound is transmitted. Sound will travel faster in warm air than in cold air. However, the speed of sound does not depend upon the frequency of the sound. If it did, you would not be able to listen to music because the high-pitched sounds would arrive at your ear at a different time than the low-pitched sounds.

The speed of light is much greater than the speed of sound. You may have had the experience of seeing a lightning flash and then, seconds later, hearing the thunder. The lightning and thunder occur at the same time, but the sound of the thunder takes much longer to reach your ears. You will use this principle to calculate the speed of sound. You will perform an experiment similar to one performed by French scientists in 1738. They set up a cannon on a hill and timed the interval between the flash and the sound. Since they knew the distance and the time, they could calculate the speed of sound.

In this investigation you will determine the speed of sound in air.

Problem

How can the speed of sound be determined?

Materials (per group)

drum
stopwatch capable of timing to a tenth of a second
measuring rope marked off in meters

Be sure to make arrangements to perform this investigation outdoors in a very large open area.

In order to involve as many students as possible, you may want to obtain additional stopwatches, have many students act as timekeepers, and then average the results.

Procedure

1. This experiment must be conducted outdoors. Select an area such as an open field or a long, lightly traveled road.

2. With the measuring rope (or a bicycle equipped with a metric odometer), measure a distance of 100 m in a straight line.
   Note: *You may want to substitute a 10m rope for the 100m rope.*

3. One pair of students should stand at the beginning of this measured distance and the other at the end, as shown in Figure 1.

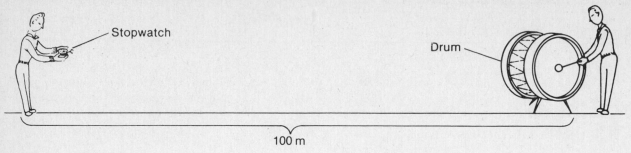

Figure 1

4. The first pair of students should create a loud, short noise by striking the drum.

5. The other pair of students should start the stopwatch precisely when they see the drum being struck. They should stop the watch precisely when they hear the noise.

6. Make two trials and record the times to a tenth of a second in the Data Table.

7. Change places with the other group and repeat the experiment. (This will eliminate any effect of wind in one direction.) Record your results in the Data Table.

Observations

DATA TABLE

Trial	Time (sec)
1	
2	
3	
4	

The times should all be near 2.9 sec.

Analysis and Conclusions

1. Average the four times and calculate the speed of sound by dividing the distance by the average time. At 20°C, the speed of sound is 344 m/sec.

2. What factors might have caused variations in the results of your four trials?
Answers will vary.

Critical Thinking and Application

1. Explain how you could determine how far from you lightning struck if you knew the speed of sound and had a stopwatch. <u>You could determine the length of time between seeing the</u> <u>flash of lightning and hearing the thunder. Sound travels about 344 m each second. Using this, you could</u> <u>calculate how far away the lightning struck.</u>

2. When fireworks burst in the sky, will you hear the explosion or see the color first? Explain. <u>You will see the color first because light travels faster than sound.</u>

3. In early movies, the sounds spoken by the characters on the screen did not match the movement of their lips, but instead lagged behind. Based on this investigation, suggest a possible explanation for this. <u>The viewer would see the image before hearing the sound. Thus if both</u> <u>were produced at the same time, the sound track would lag behind the speech movements of the screen</u> <u>characters.</u>

4. Sound travels faster in liquids than in gases, and faster in solids than in liquids. Explain why a worker who puts one ear against a long metal pipe would hear two sounds if another worker struck the pipe only once at some distance away.

   <u>The listener would first hear the sound transmitted through the iron and then the sound transmitted</u>

   <u>through the air.</u>

Going Further

Suspend a bell or alarm clock inside a large jar from which air can be evacuated by a pump. Observe what happens to the sound of the bell or alarm as the air is sucked out. Observe the speed of sound through other materials such as water or iron.

© Prentice-Hall, Inc.

————— *Laboratory Investigation* —————

57

Getting the Most From the Sun

You may want to refer students to pages 646–656 in their textbook for a general discussion of the electromagnetic spectrum.

Time required: 45 minutes—2 hours

Background Information

Most of the energy received and used on Earth comes from the sun. Although the most obvious form of the sun's energy is the light you see, this is only part of the sun's electromagnetic energy. Much of the energy is in the form of ultraviolet waves and infrared waves. This is why sunlight makes you feel warm.

In this investigation you will measure the heating effects of the sun and see how different materials change these effects.

Problem

How can the amount of energy obtained from sunlight be increased and decreased?

Materials *(per group)*

3 identical jars
black paper
aluminum foil
tape
3 Celsius thermometers
sand

Procedure

1. Fill each of the three jars with sand.

2. Wrap one jar completely with black paper, including the top, and tape the paper in place.

3. Cover the second jar with aluminum foil, including the top, and tape the foil in place.

4. Record the temperature on each of the three thermometers. Be sure all three indicate the same temperature.

5. Insert one thermometer into the sand in each jar. With the two covered jars, puncture a hole in the top covering and insert the thermometer through the hole.

6. Place all three jars in direct sunlight.

7. Record the temperature of each of the thermometers every 15 minutes for about 2 hours.

Observations

Time (min)	Temperature of Jar 1 Uncovered (°C)	Temperature of Jar 2 Covered in Black (°C)	Temperature of Jar 3 Covered in Foil (°C)
0			
15			
30			
45			
60 (1 hr)			
75			
90			
105			
120 (2 hr)			

Analysis and Conclusions

1. What is the purpose of the uncovered jar?

   The uncovered jar of sand provides a control.

2. How do the temperatures of the thermometers compare over time?

   The temperature of the jar with the black surface should increase noticeably faster than that of the other two.

3. How is the energy of sunlight carried to the sand in the jars? What type of electromagnetic radiation is mostly responsible for heating the sand?

   The energy of the sun is carried as electromagnetic waves. Infrared waves are responsible for heating.

4. What can you say about the effect of a black surface and a shiny surface on absorption of energy from the sun?

Black surfaces absorb energy. Silver surfaces do not absorb energy.

Critical Thinking and Application

1. Would the investigation have had the same conclusions if you had used a material other than sand? Explain.

Yes, however, the material may change temperature at a different rate.

2. Certain materials are designed to take advantage of the properties you saw in this investigation. For example, the glass windows of many buildings are coated with a thin layer of silver to keep the inside of the building cool. What are other black and silver materials and what are their uses?

Answers will vary. Be sure that the color of the material is related to the absorption of energy.

3. On a sunny day, would you expect the interior of a black car or a silver car to be warmer? Explain.

The interior of a black car will be warmer because black absorbs energy. The liners of swimming pools

are sometimes black to keep the water warm.

4. Using what you have learned from this investigation, explain why astronauts wear silver clothing in space.

Silver clothing protects astronauts from the direct rays of the sun.

© Prentice-Hall, Inc.

Going Further

Remove the jars from the sunlight and continue to record the temperatures of the three thermometers for 2 more hours. How do the temperatures compare? What can you say about the effect of a black surface and a shiny surface on heat loss?

Laboratory Investigation

Chapter 26   Light and Its Uses

58

Plane Mirror Images

You may want to refer students to pages 671–674 in their textbook for a general discussion of reflection and mirrors.

Time required: 35 minutes

Background Information

The image of an object formed by a plane, or flat, mirror seems to be exactly like the object. But is the image really an exact "copy" of the object? And how does a mirror produce an image?

In this investigation you will see how a plane mirror forms an image and how that image compares to the object.

Problem

How is an image produced by a plane mirror?

Materials (_per student_)

cardboard (approximately
     30 cm × 30 cm)
30-cm ruler
3 straight pins
protractor
unlined paper
small mirror and
     support

Procedure

🔥 **1.** Place the paper on the cardboard. Stand the mirror in the center of the paper and draw a line along the edge of the mirror. Stick a pin in the paper and cardboard about 4 cm in front of the mirror. Draw a small circle around the pin position and label it Object. See Figure 1.

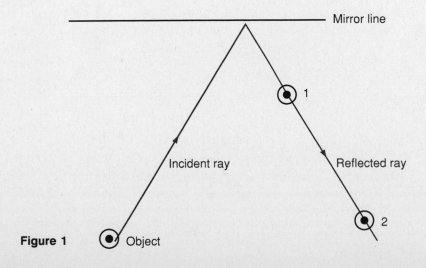

Figure 1

2. Bend down so that your head is near the lower right corner of the paper. Look at the mirror with one eye closed and observe the reflection of the pin. Do not look at the real pin. Place a pin in the paper so that it hides the reflection of the object pin in the mirror. Draw a small circle around the pin position and label it 1.

3. From the same position on the righthand side of the paper, place a second pin in the paper so that it hides the real pin you placed in position 1 and the reflection of the object pin. Draw a small circle around the pin position and label it 2.

4. Remove the pins from positions 1 and 2. Use them to repeat steps 2 and 3 from the lower left corner of the paper. Draw circles around these pin positions and label them 3 and 4.

5. Remove the mirror and all the pins. Using the ruler, draw a solid line through pin positions 1 and 2 and extend it as far as the mirror line. This line is a reflected ray. Draw a line from the object position to the point where the reflected ray leaves the mirror. This line is the incident ray. Label each ray and use an arrow on the ray to show its direction.

6. Repeat step 5 for pin positions 3 and 4.

7. Draw two lines perpendicular to the mirror line at the two points where the incident rays and the reflected rays touch. These lines are the normals. Label and measure the angles of incidence and reflection for the rays coming from the left and right corners of the paper. See Figure 2.

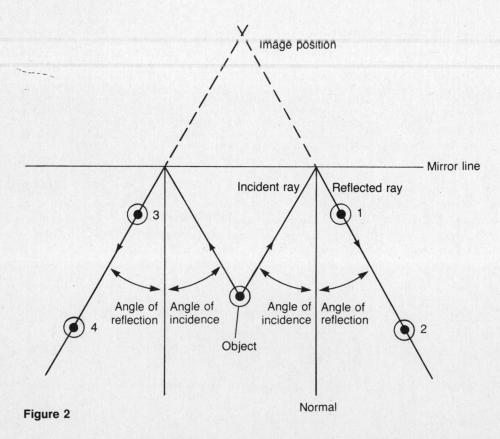

Figure 2

8. Using the ruler, draw two dashed lines extending the two reflected rays beyond the mirror line. Continue your dashed lines just beyond the point where they cross. This point is the position of the image of the pin in the mirror. Label this point Image.

Observations

    1. Attach your drawing.

                          Answers will vary.   Answers will vary.

    2. Left-side rays: Angle of incidence = _____ Angle of reflection = _____

                          Answers will vary.   Answers will vary.

    3. Right-side rays: Angle of incidence = _____ Angle of reflection = _____

Analysis and Conclusions

    1. At what distance is the object from the mirror line? About 4 cm.

    2. At what distance is the image from the mirror line? About 4 cm.

    3. How do the distances of the object and image from the mirror compare?

       They are the same.

    4. How do the angle of incidence and the angle of reflection compare in size

       a. for the rays from the left side of the paper? They are the same.

       b. for the rays from the right side of the paper? They are the same.

Critical Thinking and Application

    1. Follow the path of one of the incident rays to the mirror and of its reflected ray. Repeat for the other incident ray. If the incident ray enters from the left, the reflected ray leaves toward the right_____. If the incident ray enters from the right, the reflected ray leaves toward the left_____.

    2. Based on your answer to question 1, how does the image compare with the object?

       The image is reversed left to right.

    3. If the angle of incidence were not equal to the angle of reflection, would that have an effect on the appearance of the image? Yes. Explain. The image would not be clear. It would appear to be distorted.

4. When you look in a plane mirror, the image seems to be "inside" or "behind" the mirror. Yet an examination of the mirror reveals that the back is opaque. That is, no light rays can pass through it. What kind of image is not formed by real light rays?

A virtual image.

Why does the image seem to be "inside" or "behind" the mirror?

The reflected rays appear to be coming from behind the mirror. They appear to be coming from the point

where the extensions of the reflected rays cross.

Going Further

Investigate the types of images formed by convex and concave mirrors. How do the images formed by these curved mirrors compare to the actual objects? Find some practical applications of these mirrors.

——— *Laboratory Investigation* ———

Chapter 26   Light and Its Uses

59

Refraction of Light

You may want to refer students to pages 675–680 in their textbook for a general discussion of refraction.

Time required: 40 minutes

Background Information

You have probably observed that a pencil in a half-filled glass of water appears to be broken at the point where the air and water meet. This happens because rays of light passing from one substance into another substance of different density change their direction of motion. The rays bend, or refract. An observer sees the light rays bend as they pass from one substance to another. In the case of the "broken" pencil, the rays of light coming from the pencil in the water bend as they pass from the water to the air. As a result, the pencil appears to be broken.

In this investigation you will observe the refraction, or bending, of light as it passes through a glass plate having parallel sides.

Problem

How do light rays behave as they pass through substances of different densities?

Materials *(per student)*

cardboard (approx. 30 cm × 30 cm)
glass plate (7 cm × 7 cm × 6 cm thick)
4 straight pins
protractor
ruler
unlined paper

Procedure

1. Place the paper on the cardboard. Place the glass plate in the center of the paper so that the transparent edges are at the top and bottom. Draw a line around the glass plate.

2. Using your ruler, draw a line on your paper at an angle to the top of the glass plate. Do not draw this line perpendicular to the plate. See Figure 1.

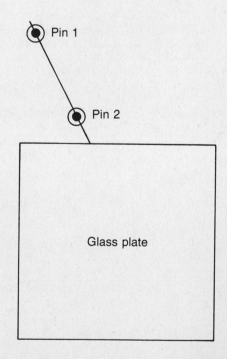

Figure 1   Eye

© Prentice-Hall, Inc.

3. Place two pins on the line about 3 cm apart. Draw circles around the base of the pins and label the circles Pin 1 and Pin 2. Bend down and look through the bottom edge of the glass plate until you see Pins 1 and 2 positioned exactly behind each other. (They will look like only one pin.)

4. Place two more pins on the lower part of your paper so that they also seem to line up with Pins 1 and 2. (All four pins should appear to be one pin.) Draw circles around the base of these pins and label them Pin 3 and Pin 4.

5. Remove the pins and the glass plate. Using a ruler, draw a line through the positions of Pins 3 and 4 just to where they meet the line made by the glass plate.

6. The line through Pins 1 and 2 represents a ray of light entering the glass plate and is called the incident ray. Label this ray and draw arrows on it to show its direction of motion.

7. The line through Pins 3 and 4 represents a ray of light leaving the glass plate and going to your eye. It is called the emergent ray. Label this ray and draw arrows on it to show its direction of motion.

8. Using your ruler, connect the incident ray and the emergent ray through the glass plate. This line is called the refracted ray. Label this ray and draw arrows on it to show its direction of motion.

9. Using a protractor, construct perpendiculars to the side of the glass plate at the points where the incident and emergent rays touch it. These lines are called normals. Extend the normals into the glass plate area. You should have formed two angles on each side of the glass plate.

10. Two angles are formed with the normal as the incident ray touches the side of the plate and as the refracted ray touches the side of the plate. These two angles are called angles of incidence. Label these two angles I.

11. Two angles are formed with the normal as the refracted ray moves through the glass plate and again as the emergent ray leaves the plate. These two angles are called angles of refraction. Label these two angles R.

12. Measure the angles of incidence and the angles of refraction and record your measurements in Observations.

13. Using your ruler and a dashed line, extend the emergent ray backward through the glass plate and beyond it.

Observations

1. Attach your completed ray diagram.   See sample completed ray diagram.

2. Pins 1 and 2: Angle of Incidence ___Answers will vary.___ Angle of Refraction ___Answers will vary.___

3. Pins 3 and 4: Angle of Incidence ___Answers will vary.___ Angle of Refraction ___Answers will vary.___

Analysis and Conclusions

1. As the incident ray enters the glass, how does it bend with respect to the normal?

It bends toward the normal.

2. As the emergent ray leaves the glass, how does it bend with respect to the normal?

It bends away from the normal.

3. How do the two angles of incidence compare?

They are the same.

4. How do the two angles of refraction compare?

They are the same.

5. What do the emergent ray and the incident ray have in common?

They are parallel to each other.

Critical Thinking and Application

1. Why does the light ray bend as it passes from air to glass or from glass to air?

When a ray of light passes from one substance to a substance of different density, it bends. This is

because its speed changes.

2. In this investigation, the refracted ray can also be the incident ray. Why? *Hint:* Turn the

drawing upside down. The refracted ray leaves the glass plate at the same angle that the incident ray

enters it.

3. Suppose you try to retrieve a coin that has fallen into an aquarium. Looking down into the water, you see the coin and reach for it, but find it is not where it appears to be.

Why? The light rays coming from the coin to your eye bend as they pass from the water to the air. So

the coin is not where it appears to be.

© Prentice-Hall, Inc.

Going Further

Repeat this investigation using a glass triangle instead of a square glass plate. Measure the angles of incidence and refraction as you did in this investigation. How do the angles of incidence and refraction compare? How do your results compare with those for the square glass? Form a hypothesis to account for any differences you might observe.

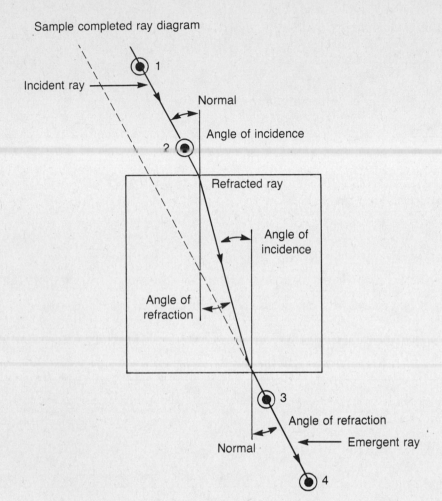

Sample completed ray diagram

Incident ray

Normal

Angle of incidence

Refracted ray

Angle of incidence

Angle of refraction

Angle of refraction

Normal

Emergent ray

Laboratory Investigation

Chapter 26   Light and Its Uses

60

Observing Refraction of Light

You may want to refer students to pages 675–680 in their textbook for a general discussion of refraction and lenses.

Time required: 40 minutes

Background Information

When light passes at an angle from air to a denser substance such as glass, the light rays bend. The bending of light is called refraction. Lenses refract, or bend, light. Convex lenses, which are thicker in the middle than at the edges, cause light to converge at a focal point. Concave lenses, which are thinner in the middle, cause light to diverge, or spread out.

The images formed by refracted light are either real or virtual images. Real images can be focused on a screen. Virtual images cannot. In this investigation you will compare the images formed by convex and concave lenses.

Problem

How do convex and concave lenses refract light?

Materials *(per group)*

convex lens with focal point of
    10–15 cm*
concave lens*
image screen*
light source**
meterstick with support stands*
lens holder*
light source holder*
screen holder*

*All these materials are found in science catalogs under the heading Optical Bench Accessories.
**A simple light source is a 15-watt bulb with a piece of cardboard in front of it. If you cut an L-shaped opening in the cardboard, the image will clearly indicate whether inversion has occurred.

Procedure

1. Set up the optical bench as shown in Figure 1. Use the convex lens. How can you tell which is the convex lens? The convex lens is thicker in the middle. _____

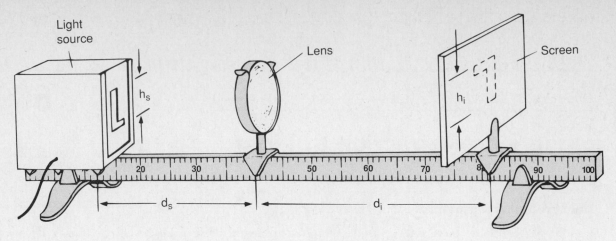

Light source

Lens

Screen

h_s

h_i

20   30   50   60   70   8   90   100

d_s

d_i

Figure 1

Time can be saved by simply giving the students the focal length of the lens. If students do not have ready access to an outside light source, step 2 will have to be omitted.

2. Determine the focal length of your lens by removing the light source and pointing the lens and screen toward an unshaded window. Slide the screen along the meterstick until a clear image of an outside tree, car, house, or other object is visible. Measure in centimeters the focal length (distance between the screen and the lens). Record the focal length in the Data Table.

3. Place the screen at one end of the meterstick and the light source at the opposite end.

4. Slide the lens until it is 5 cm more than twice the focal length from the light source. Slide the image screen along the meterstick until a well-defined image appears. Record the following in the Data Table. (a) whether the image is erect or inverted; (b) distance (d_s) from the light source to the lens; (c) distance (d_i) from the lens to the image; (d) height (h_s) of the light source; (e) height (h_i) of the image.

5. Repeat step 4, but this time slide the lens until it is exactly twice the focal length from the light source. Be sure to record the results in the Data Table.

6. Repeat step 4 again, but this time slide the lens until it is less than two focal lengths but more than one focal length from the light source. Record your results in the Data Table.

7. Position the lens so that it is exactly one focal length from the light source. Can an image be formed? No.

8. Position the lens less than one focal length from the light source. Can an image be formed? No.

9. Remove the screen and look at the light source through the lens.

Observation Enlarged image, right side up.

10. Replace the convex lens with the concave lens. Repeat step 9.

Observation Smaller image, right side up.

11. Slide the lens 10 cm farther from the light source.

Observation The image decreases in size.

260

Name _____ Class _____ Date _____

Observations

DATA TABLE

Focal length of lens: $\underline{15}$				
d_s (cm)	d_i (cm)	h_s (cm)	h_i (cm)	Erect or Inverted
35.0	27.0	1.6	1.0	Inverted
30.0	31.0	1.6	1.6	Inverted
23.0	45.0	1.6	3.0	Inverted

(Possible answers)

Analysis and Conclusions

1. As the distance (d_s) between the convex lens and the source decreased, did the distance (d_i) between the lens and the image decrease or increase?

   Increase.

2. As d_s decreased, did the height (h_i) of the image decrease or increase?

   Increase.

3. At what distance (d_s) must the lens be placed in order for the image height (h_i) to be equal to the source height (h_s)? Express your answer in terms of the number of focal lengths (1f, 2f, 2.5f). 2f

4. Can a real image be produced when the lens is placed at or less than a focal length's distance from the source? No.

5. Does the concave lens produce a real or a virtual image?

   Virtual.

6. Does the size of the image in a concave lens increase or decrease as the lens is moved away from the source? Decrease.

Critical Thinking and Application

1. Explain how the lenses in eyeglasses help nearsighted and farsighted people see better.

   The lenses can alter the focal length of the lens of the eye so that images will become clear at either a

   greater or lesser distance.

2. Why might a photographer have to change lenses when taking a close-up shot?

The focal length of the long-distance lens might be too great to focus on an image that is close to the

camera.

3. An optical instrument is producing upside-down images. What might be the problem?

A convex instead of concave lens might be in use, or perhaps the image is being viewed to produce a

real rather than a virtual image.

4. How might lenses be used to produce the images in a funhouse mirror?

By using lenses of different focal lengths, the mirrors can be made to produce images that are upside

down or larger or smaller than usual.

Going Further

Find out what kind of lens is used in a refracting telescope and how it operates to produce an image of a distant object.

Laboratory Investigation

61

Constructing a Pinhole Viewer and a Periscope

You may want to refer students to pages 689–692 in their textbook for a general discussion of optical instruments.

Time required: Part A—20 minutes
Part B—40 minutes

Background Information

Light travels in straight lines. This enables scientists to predict its behavior during reflection and refraction. Many instruments and devices make use of this property. In this investigation you will construct two such devices: a pinhole viewer and a periscope.

Part A   Pinhole Viewer   *You may want to have students do all or part of this investigation as a take-home project.*

Problem

How does a pinhole viewer work?

You may want to punch the holes in the cans required in this lab before the lab period. The size of the oak tag used in Part B should
Materials *(per group)*   *be such that the mirrors fit as in Figure 2.*

small juice or coffee can (with plastic top, if possible) with a small (approximately 1 mm), clean, round hole punched into the center of the closed end

rubber band
piece of waxed paper or tracing paper slightly larger than the open end of the can

candle and matches
piece of cardboard (6 cm × 6 cm)

Procedure

1. Hold the can up to your eye and look through it. Make certain the hole punched in it is small, clean, and centered.

2. Place the piece of translucent waxed or tracing paper over the open end of the can and use the rubber band to fasten it in place.

🔥 3. Light the candle and place a few drops of wax on the small piece of cardboard. Then place the candle onto it so that it will remain upright.

4. Position the candle and cardboard on the top of the lab table.

5. Hold the pinhole viewer so that the pinhole points toward the lighted candle. Position the viewer so that an image of the candle is clearly seen on the translucent paper screen. (Lights in the classroom may have to be shut off and the shades drawn for this part of the lab investigation.) Draw the image of the lighted candle in Drawing 1.

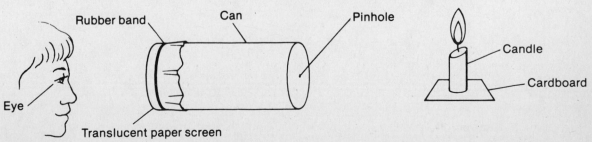

Figure 1

© Prentice-Hall, Inc.   **263**

Observations

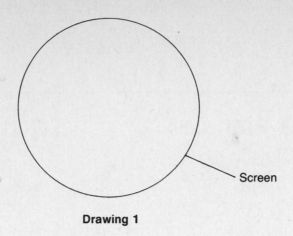

Screen

Drawing 1

Analysis and Conclusions

1. Is the image in Drawing 1 right side up or upside down?

Upside down.

2. If the lighted candle is so much larger than the pinhole, how is it that the image is

formed on the translucent screen? The light rays are focused by the pinhole and the image appears

on the screen.

Critical Thinking and Application

1. How could this pinhole viewer be changed into a pinhole camera? Be as specific as you

can. Include drawings if you wish. You could place film where the screen is and have a shutter

expose the film for a short time.

2. In Drawing 2, draw what you think is the path the rays of light take from the lighted
candle to form the image on the translucent screen. Use a straight edge (ruler) when you
draw the rays of light.

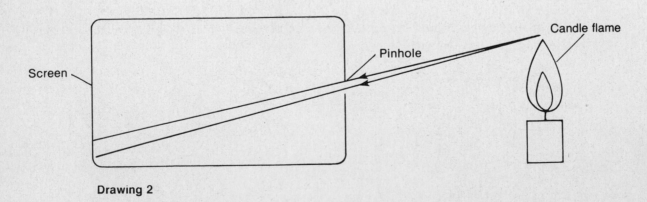

Candle flame

Pinhole

Screen

Drawing 2

Part B Periscope

Problem

How does a periscope work?

Materials (*per group*)

scissors
oak tag (heavy grade)
2 small pocket mirrors
rubber cement

Procedure

1. Draw the solid lines on the oak tag as shown in Figure 2.

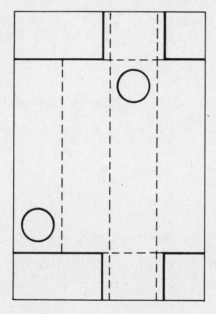
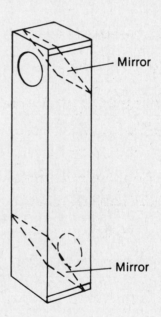

Mirror

Mirror

Figure 2

2. Using the scissors, carefully cut along the solid lines to create the frame and openings for your periscope.

3. Fold the oak tag along the dotted lines as shown in Figure 2.

4. Using rubber cement, glue the small mirrors in place before gluing the top and bottom closed.

5. Test your periscope by getting below the level of your desk or laboratory table and sighting the candle. You might also see if you can observe objects around corners or out in the corridor.

Observations

Draw the way light rays travel
in a periscope in Drawing 3.

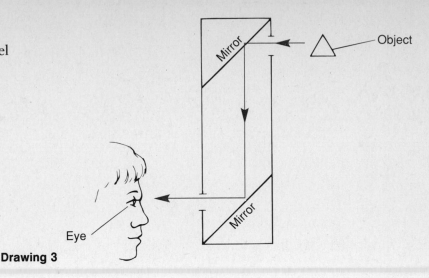

Drawing 3

Analysis and Conclusions

1. Does a periscope demonstrate that light travels in straight lines, even though it enables you to see around corners? Explain your answer.

   Yes, the light rays still travel in straight lines but are reflected at an angle so that you can see around

   corners or over objects.

2. What would happen to the image if only the mirror near the opening of the periscope were used? The image would "die" at the bottom of the tube.

Critical Thinking and Application

1. What must be true about the angles of the two mirrors used in a periscope? Why?

   The angles of the mirrors must be the same so that the angles of reflection will be the same. Otherwise

   the light from the second image might miss the eye hole.

2. Suppose you are hiking along the side of a mountain and want to send a flashlight signal to someone who has just rounded a bend in the trail. How might you do it?

   Hold a mirror in one hand and a flashlight in the other hand. Hold the mirror at an angle and shine the

   flashlight on it so that the light is reflected around the side of the mountain.

Going Further

1. Develop a pinhole camera that has a shutter and a film holder on the back. Use a cartridge-type film. Take pictures of objects in bright sunlight.

2. Make a device that is a combination of a pinhole camera and a periscope that will enable you to take a picture of an object even though it is not directly in your sight.